Prestwick House
Vocabulary
Power Plus

Vocabulary, Reading, and Writing Exercises

Prestwick House

P.O. Box 658 • Clayton, DE 19938
(800) 932-4593 • www.prestwickhouse.com

ISBN 978-1-62019-274-0

Project Editor:
Daniel Reed

Senior Editor:
Paul Moliken

Production Editor:
Darlene Gilmore

Contributing Editors:
Lisa Tetrault
Leah Rodriguez
Rachel Natbony

Contributors:
James Wohr
Sydney Palmer
Allison Billmire
Alana Domingo

Layout:
Jeremy Clark

Art and Design:
Larry Knox

Prestwick House

Copyright © 2017 by Prestwick House, Inc.

Printed in the United States of America.

ISBN: 978-1-62019-274-0

Item No. 310229

Vocabulary Power Plus

LEVEL 5

Vocabulary, Reading, and Writing Exercises

Table of Contents

Introduction

How many words do you know?

100 words?

1,000 words?

10,000 words?

Believe it or not, you will probably know more than 15,000 words by the time you grow up.

Yes, you are that smart. And it's a great thing. Just one little word can express an idea that you might need dozens of other words to describe. For example, explain what *love* or *happiness* is without using those two words. It might take a while, especially if you want people to truly understand the ideas the words represent.

Imagine talking to a group of two- or three-year-old toddlers. They very well may know 1,000 words. If you ask them what they think about something, the answer will be long and, possibly, difficult to understand.

You, older and knowing 5,000 words, have words to describe your idea more clearly. You could answer the same question in seconds instead of minutes. Your answer will probably be much clearer, too. It is even possible that you know a single word that expresses everything the toddlers described.

For the rest of your life, the more words you learn, the better you will be able to communicate. Whether you speak your ideas out loud or write them down on paper, your personal library of words will make your ideas clear and concise. People will understand you, and you will understand other people.

We hope *Vocabulary Power Plus* gives you a great start to building your collection of words. The meanings of words overlap in many ways, so the more words you learn, the better you'll become at learning new ones. The reading passages in this book will help you see how other people use words to express ideas. Some passages will ask you to improve how others use their words.

Have fun, and take pride in building your word library. As your ideas get bigger and bigger, you'll need plenty of words to express them!

Pronunciation Guide

A	add, mat
AH	lot, ox
AR	car, tar
AW	ball, saw
AY	day, play
E, EH	d**e**vil, met
EE	eat, **e**vil
ER	b**er**ry, **er**ror
I, IH	lid, sip
IY	cry, sigh
O, OH	boat, slow
OM	bomb, mom
OO	loop, soup
OR	door, more
OW	crown, ouch
OY	oil, toy
S	miss, snake
U, UH	shut, much
UL	gull, skull
ULL	ab**le**, buck**le**
UR	p**ur**ple, sh**ir**t
ZH	trea**s**ure, colli**si**on

Word List

Lesson One
abstract
emblem
idol
improper
inferior
linger
resent
seize
sever
tragedy

Lesson Two
artificial
custom
deceive
dominant
fertile
fragrance
magnify
quarrel
rant
vicious

Lesson Three
clash
contradict
destiny
envy
ignorance
regal
rigid
sensation
substantial
tolerate

Lesson Four
acquaint
betray
chronological
dispute
federal
feeble
govern
longitude
mope
vanity

Lesson Five
decay
dissatisfied
distinguished
emigrate
facility
foe
frigid
heirloom
postpone
timid

Lesson Six
abandon
carnivore
climate
elementary
exterminate
inauguration
mellow
revolt
urban
verdict

Lesson Seven
amplify
emphasize
extravagant
finance
inspire
majority
nomad
preliminary
radiate
treacherous

Lesson Eight
commodity
hectic
intend
invincible
minority
remark
significant
site
superstition
trespass

Lesson Nine
agitate
archaeology
benefit
conscience
controversial
courteous
descendant
span
temporary
woe

Lesson Ten
confide
dejected
dishearten
entrepreneur
frontier
fugitive
inquire
proceed
swift
vast

Lesson Eleven
contrast
equivalent
feat
herbivore
misleading
obtain
rapid
superb
turnpike
vanquish

Lesson Twelve
campaign
collision
communicate
consistent
interfere
native
poverty
resolution
scarce
simulate

Lesson Thirteen
boast
efficient
feud
fury
gradual
justification
perish
preserve
qualify
stationary

Lesson Fourteen
abide
anxiety
infer
inseparable
juvenile
monitor
prevailing
prosperous
representative
salary

Lesson Fifteen
abbreviate
blockade
compromise
essential
famine
hardship
hideous
phenomenon
reside
urgent

Lesson Sixteen
apprehensive
assemble
condemn
confidential
disintegrate
hijack
patriotism
prey
responsible
tenant

Lesson Seventeen
abundant
adolescent
dwell
gauge
hygiene
impractical
irritate
modesty
outlandish
sanitary

Lesson Eighteen
ail
depart
enterprise
frank
frequent
manufacture
peculiar
spectacle
sympathy
toll

Lesson Nineteen
abode
analyze
artifact
endanger
grieve
merge
offensive
symptom
vague
wholesome

Lesson Twenty
acquire
diagram
expel
monarch
omnivore
reprimand
rural
spiritual
sufficient
superior

Lesson Twenty-One
bestow
conserve
excess
hysterical
illusion
moderate
restrain
savor
vacant
wit

Lesson One

abstract
AB-STRAKT

adj. existing only as an idea
Abstract painters use colors, shapes, and lines to show complex ideas.
syn: unreal; theoretical   *ant: actual; real*

emblem
EM-BLEM

n. an image used to represent an idea or group
The car company chose a ram as an *emblem* on its trucks to suggest that they are strong, powerful vehicles.
syn: logo; symbol

idol
IY-DUL

n. a person who is excessively admired or worshipped
I would pay a great deal of money to see my musical *idol* perform.
syn: celebrity; superstar

improper
IM-**PRAH**-PUR

adj. not correct in a given situation
Many people think it is *improper* to use a smartphone at the dinner table.
syn: unsuitable; wrong   *ant: proper; right*

inferior
IN-**FEER**-EE-UR

adj. low in value or rank
The *inferior* teams failed to make it into the championships.
syn: worse   *ant: superior; best*

linger
LIN-GUR

v. to stay in a place longer than expected or necessary
At the art museum, visitors *lingered* near the most popular sculptures.
syn: loiter   *ant: leave*

resent
REH-**ZENT**

v. to be annoyed or bitter at
You might *resent* me right now for being honest, but you will thank me one day.
ant: approve; like

seize

SEEZ

v. to take quickly by force

While I was out of the room, Walter *seized* my favorite chair.

syn: grab; capture   *ant: release*

sever

SEH-VER

v. to cut or separate a part from the whole

The table saw *severed* Ben's finger, but doctors were able to reattach it.

syn: divide; split   *ant: join; unite*

tragedy

TRA-JEH-DEE

n. a situation causing great sadness or loss

The hospital fire was a *tragedy* that made life worse for people who were already suffering.

syn: disaster   *ant: success*

Exercise I – Words in Context

Using the list of vocabulary words, supply the correct word to complete each sentence.

1. What a[n] _____ it was that the country was hit by two earthquakes in a single year.

2. The soldier's silver star medal is a[n] _____ of bravery.

3. Miranda went all the way to Canada to hear her _____ speak at a convention.

4. How to be happy is a[n] _____ idea that many people think about.

5. The princess had her workers build a moat so invaders could not _____ her castle.

6. My kitten _____ the connection between the computer and the mouse by chewing through the cord.

7. The entire 5th grade _____ Ms. Newcomb for having all the candy removed from the vending machines.

8. Audrey's old bike was just _____ when compared to her new one.

9. Sticking your chewing gum under a table is certainly a[n] _____ way to get rid of it.

10. The new student _____ by the swings until someone invited him to play ball.

Exercise II – Finish the Sentence

First, choose the ending for each sentence that makes the best sense with the italicized vocabulary word used. Then, write your own ending for each sentence that shows you understand the meaning of the vocabulary word.

1. In the fantasy novel's *abstract* world,…
  A. the main character battled criminals.
  B. animals could talk to humans.

2. Rob's jeans were *improper* clothing for the fancy dinner, so…
  A. he changed into a suit and tie.
  B. he washed them first.

3. The microwave was of *inferior* quality, and we…
  A. traded it in for a better one.
  B. could not wait to use it.

4. The computer company wanted to design an *emblem* that…
  A. allowed Internet browsers to load faster.
  B. made their company look big and dependable.

5. When the sports *idol* insulted the president,…
  A. her fans turned against her.
  B. no one really noticed.

6. After the *tragedy* caused by the hurricane, many people…
  A. went to the beach.
  B. had to rebuild their houses.

7. Sally's cold *lingered* for weeks, and…
  A. she felt like it would never go away.
  B. she took medicine for it.

8. Police *seized* Roger's car because he had…
  A. reported it missing.
  B. stolen it.

9. Abby *resented* her brother after he…

    A. helped her with her homework.

    B. was given the Christmas gift that she wanted.

10. Heidi and Gina decided to *sever* their friendship because they…

    A. spent more time arguing than having fun.

    B. really enjoyed hanging out with each other.

Exercise III – Crossword Puzzle

Use the clues and the words from this lesson to complete the crossword puzzle.

Across

2. Alyssa's biggest _____ is her mother, not some overpaid movie star.

4. The babysitter said to the toddler, "_____ behavior will make bedtime come earlier."

7. I dislike the cold and hope that summer will _____ for a few more weeks.

8. I will always _____ you for when you embarrassed me in front of my class.

9. The smartest kid I know thought getting one *B* instead of all *A*'s was a[n] _____.

Down

1. I had to tell my teacher, "I just can't picture the _____ ideas you are talking about."

2. The factory collapsed because it was built from _____ materials.

3. The science club designed a[n] _____ with some bubbling gas on it.

5. Penny's parents got divorced and _____ all contact with each other.

6. The team that can _____ the other team's flag and take it back to its base wins.

Exercise IV – Critical Reading

Carefully read the passage and then choose the best answer for each of the questions that follow. The passage contains vocabulary words from the lesson.

Copper is a shiny, reddish material used for wires, pipes, and cooking pans. Most people think of pennies when they think of copper. Few people probably think of the Statue of Liberty. But Lady Liberty is, in fact, made of copper. You wouldn't think so because of her muted green color. However, this national **emblem** wasn't always
5   green. Immigrants saw a golden-red statue on their way to Ellis Island in the late 1800s. So, why, then, is the Statue of Liberty green today?

Lady Liberty was supposed to keep its golden-red coloring. The designer, Frédéric Auguste Bartholdi, didn't think she would change color. Bartholdi decided his copper statue would be of the Roman goddess Libertas, who was one of the **idols** of the
10   American Revolution. Bartholdi, a Frenchman, wanted to honor America's freedom. He chose to create a tribute to liberty for America's hundredth birthday. He proposed the statue as a gift from France to America.

Construction of the statue started in 1876. It was built in bits and pieces. For example, the head was done in 1878. It was shown at a fair that same year. Small
15   pieces were put on display in America and France until Lady Liberty was finished and assembled in 1884. Then, workers took it apart to send it across the ocean to America. It was finally rebuilt in the United States in 1886. The Statue of Liberty still stands on Liberty Island today, though it looks a little different than it did in the 1880s.

20   Bartholdi chose copper because it is strong but light. It could be molded to form the statue's face and the folds in her robes, too. Seemingly, the only **inferior** quality of copper is the way it turns light green when exposed to water and air. Water and air cause oxidation. A patina, or a layer of green film, then forms. The statue still had a copper color until around 1900. It hadn't been exposed to enough water and air to
25   have a patina yet, but, by 1906, it was covered in a greenish-blue film.

The government thought about painting the statue to get rid of the color, but Americans liked the new greenish-blue hue, so no changes were made. Also, the patina protects the copper. Removing or covering the green color could damage the landmark. The government even found copper with similar patina to use when some of the older
30   copper had to be replaced. They looked for greenish-blue copper because it would be a **tragedy** to ruin the look of the beautiful, long-lasting statue.

Over the past hundred years, the Statue of Liberty has been carefully restored many times. Most repairs have been inside. Lady Liberty's inside was painted and had broken or loose parts replaced for safety reasons. Her exterior still remains
35   green, though. But no matter its color, the Statue of Liberty endures as a literal representation of the **abstract** concept of freedom on which the United States of America is founded.

Exercise IV – Critical Reading Questions

1. Choose the best title for the passage.
   A. Bartholdi's Major Works
   B. Lady Liberty: Golden to Green
   C. Restoring the Statue of Liberty
   D. Immigration in the 1880s
   E. Lady Liberty at the World's Fair

2. In line 11, *tribute* most nearly means
   A. complaint
   B. present
   C. product
   D. sacrifice
   E. memorial

3. What is the purpose of paragraph 4 (lines 20-25)?
   A. to describe the design of the statue
   B. to discuss Bartholdi's life
   C. to show restoration efforts
   D. to explain how the statue turned green
   E. to give the history of the statue

4. The author of this passage would probably agree that
   A. America should not have accepted the Statue of Liberty as a gift.
   B. The Statue of Liberty should stay green.
   C. Lady Liberty should not be restored.
   D. Bartholdi was not a good designer.
   E. Building the Statue of Liberty took too long.

5. Choose the statement that provides evidence to support your answer to the previous question.
   A. "They looked for greenish-blue copper because it would be a tragedy to ruin the look of the beautiful, long-lasting statue." (lines 30-31)
   B. "Bartholdi decided his copper statue would be of the Roman goddess Libertas, who was one of the idols of the American Revolution." (lines 8-10)
   C. "Over the past hundred years, the Statue of Liberty has been carefully restored many times." (lines 32-33)
   D. "Then, workers took it apart to send it across the ocean to America." (lines 16-17)
   E. "A patina, or a layer of green film, then forms." (line 23)

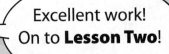

Lesson Two

artificial
AR-TIH-**FIH**-SHULL

adj. made by people; not found in nature
The candy is full of *artificial* flavors and colors, not real fruit.
syn: synthetic; unnatural   ant: genuine; real

custom
KUS-TUM

n. the usual way of doing something; typical behavior
Our family's *custom* on Thanksgiving is to invite our neighbors over to celebrate.
syn: habit; tradition

deceive
DIH-**SEEV**

v. to trick by lying
Lin's gorilla costume was not realistic enough to *deceive* anyone in the neighborhood.
syn: mislead; delude

dominant
DAH-MIH-NINT

adj. having the most power or control
Since she talked more than her sisters, we could tell Anita was the *dominant* sibling.
syn: commanding   ant: submissive

fertile
FUR-TILL

adj. capable of sustaining life or reproduction
I live in the desert, where there is very little *fertile* land available.
syn: fruitful   ant: barren; sterile

fragrance
FRAY-GRENSE

n. a sweet, pleasant smell
The *fragrances* began at the perfume counter and drifted through the whole store.
syn: scent

magnify
MAG-NIH-FIY

v. to make something appear larger in size or importance
Marshall *magnified* a photo of Mars that he took with his camera.
syn: enlarge; enhance   ant: reduce; lessen

quarrel
KWAR-ULL

n. an argument
The two squirrels had a bit of a *quarrel* over the last acorn in the field.
syn: disagreement; fight   ant: agreement

rant
RANT

v. to speak angrily and wildly
Paul *ranted* for hours about the noisy highway the state built next to his house.
syn: rave

vicious
VIH-SHUS

adj. extremely violent and cruel
Very often, dogs that act *vicious* are afraid of, not angered by, visitors.
syn: savage; wicked   ant: gentle; kind

Exercise I – Words in Context

Using the list of vocabulary words, supply the correct word to complete each sentence.

1. My sister and I had a[n] _____ about who would get the last taco.

2. Adding nutrients will make the soil for your potted plant more _____.

3. I know that the bracelet looks expensive, but the jewels on it are _____.

4. The artist drew a silly picture of my face that _____ my eyes to twice their normal size.

5. Horace is left-handed, so his left hand is the _____ one.

6. On April Fools' Day, many kids tried to _____ their friends by telling silly lies.

7. The _____ old woman took enjoyment from hurting other people's feelings.

8. The candle's strong pine _____ gave me a headache.

9. Is it a[n] _____ in your town to watch fireworks on Independence Day?

10. Bobby couldn't stop _____ about the mistake that cost his favorite football team the game.

Exercise II – Finish the Sentence

First, choose the ending for each sentence that makes the best sense with the italicized vocabulary word used. Then, write your own ending for each sentence that shows you understand the meaning of the vocabulary word.

1. Alice now keeps only *artificial* plants, since…
   A. fake plants don't smell as nice.
   B. her real plants usually die.

2. The company created a workplace that was *fertile* for ideas by…
   A. asking everybody for their opinions.
   B. having only the boss make decisions.

3. The sheriff warned tourists that a *vicious* alligator…
   A. lived in the lake, but it wouldn't hurt anyone.
   B. sometimes snaps at people near the water.

4. The sergeant knew that the *dominant* soldier…
   A. would be the best leader for the squad.
   B. did not have much self-confidence.

5. One *custom* Jaqui really liked was…
   A. a week of travel for spring vacation.
   B. making sure to wear his retainer.

6. Despite their *quarrel* in the morning, the couple…
   A. felt much more awake during the afternoon.
   B. hugged and said they loved each other later.

7. When the house filled with the *fragrance* of baking cookies,…
   A. the children's mouths watered.
   B. Doug complained about the noise.

8. The trouble with my broken-down car was *magnified* when…
   A. someone loaned me her cell phone to call for help.
   B. the engine caught on fire.

9. After the car dealer *deceived* a customer into buying a car with problems,...

   A. the dealer closed up his business.

   B. a judge ordered him to return the customer's money.

10. As Mr. Parkhill *ranted* about the government again, his coworkers…

   A. felt inspired by his kind words.

   B. told him to stop complaining.

Exercise III – Crossword Puzzle

Use the clues and the words from this lesson to complete the crossword puzzle.

Across

5. Last week, the most _____ team unexpectedly lost 10-0.

6. Don't _____ to everyone about your unfair treatment; think about others who aren't as lucky as you are.

8. Nick's _____ smile in the photo does not match his sad eyes.

9. I heard my sisters' _____ over who should get the new laptop and who would keep the old one.

10. I enjoy the _____ of giving candy on Valentine's Day.

Down

1. It was impossible to _____ my dad about anything; he already knew my tricks.

2. The _____ of the lilacs lasted all summer.

3. Our _____ garden gives us hundreds of tomatoes every year.

4. Hold the lens closer to your eyes to _____ the tiny letters.

7. Lonnie used pepper spray to stop the big dog's _____ attack on the cat.

Exercise IV – Critical Reading

Carefully read the passage and then choose the best answer for each of the questions that follow. The passage contains vocabulary words from the lesson.

In 2016, botanists around the United States were taken by surprise when titan arum, a tropical plant native to Indonesia, started to bloom in seven different gardens and greenhouses across the country. The event surprised botanists because titan arum flowers bloom only once every six years. Before and after blooming, they
5   are completely inactive. But they do absorb nutrients from their **fertile** soil. Plants cultivated in the **artificial** conditions of a greenhouse bloom even less often, usually once every eight to ten years.

But when it does bloom, what a flower it is! Titan arum produces the largest flowering structure in the world. It can grow over eight feet tall and three feet
10   around. Technically, it is not one flower but many small flowers on the base of a tall stalk. The stalk is surrounded by a large, purple covering that looks like an upside-down skirt. This **dominant** petal-like part causes the bloom to look like a single, giant flower.

The titan arum is odd in other ways as well. Instead of having a pleasant
15   **fragrance**, it smells like rotting meat and fish. This stench has earned titan arum the name "corpse flower." The foul odor **deceives** flies into thinking they are about to feast on a dead animal. The maroon, blood color of the plant further convinces the insects that the corpse flower is a good source of food. The bugs are fooled. They fly inside the bloom and pollinate it. To humans, however, the smell is far from
20   inviting. The enclosed space of a greenhouse seems to **magnify** the stink. Luckily for the people who **rant** about the disgusting smell, the corpse flower blooms for only one day before it wilts. Then, the tall stalk collapses and the petal-like cover shrivels inward. Over the next few months, the plant will become dormant again as it regains the energy it needs to grow such a large, stinky bloom.

25   Scientists have limited opportunities to study corpse flowers, so they still have much to learn about the species. No one knows why so many corpse flowers bloomed at the same time, but they have some theories. Many of the titan arums in the United States grew from seeds distributed to growers between 2002 and 2008. One professor thinks that the seeds could have been from related plants, so they share similar
30   blooming cycles. A simpler reason is that more greenhouses in the United States grow titan arums these days, so there are more plants that could bloom within a given year. If that's the case, botanical gardens may see corpse flowers, in all their smelly glory, more often than they have in the past.

Exercise IV – Critical Reading Questions

1. As used in line 6, the word *cultivated* most nearly means
    A. thought.
    B. removed.
    C. buried.
    D. picked.
    E. grown.

2. Titan arums produce their specific smell in order to
    A. indicate that they are poisonous.
    B. get hummingbirds to feed on them.
    C. lure in insects on which to feed.
    D. attract flies to pollinate them.
    E. discourage animals from eating them.

3. After the bloom wilts, a titan arum
    A. goes dormant.
    B. dies off gradually.
    C. grows taller.
    D. sprouts leaves.
    E. produces another flower.

4. Why is it difficult for scientists to study titan arums extensively?
    A. The plants live in the dense Indonesian jungle.
    B. The rare blooms last only one day.
    C. The strong odor makes it difficult to focus.
    D. Only a few greenhouses grow them.
    E. The small flowers are hidden by a covering.

5. Choose the line from the passage that provides evidence that supports your answer to the previous question.
    A. "…started to bloom in seven different gardens and greenhouses across the country." (lines 2-3)
    B. "…many small flowers on the base of a tall stalk…surrounded by a large, purple covering…" (lines 10-11)
    C. "…the corpse flower blooms for only one day before it wilts." (lines 21-22)
    D. "…botanists around the United States were taken by surprise when titan arum, a tropical plant native to Indonesia…" (lines 1-2)
    E. "To humans, however, the smell is far from inviting." (lines 19-20)

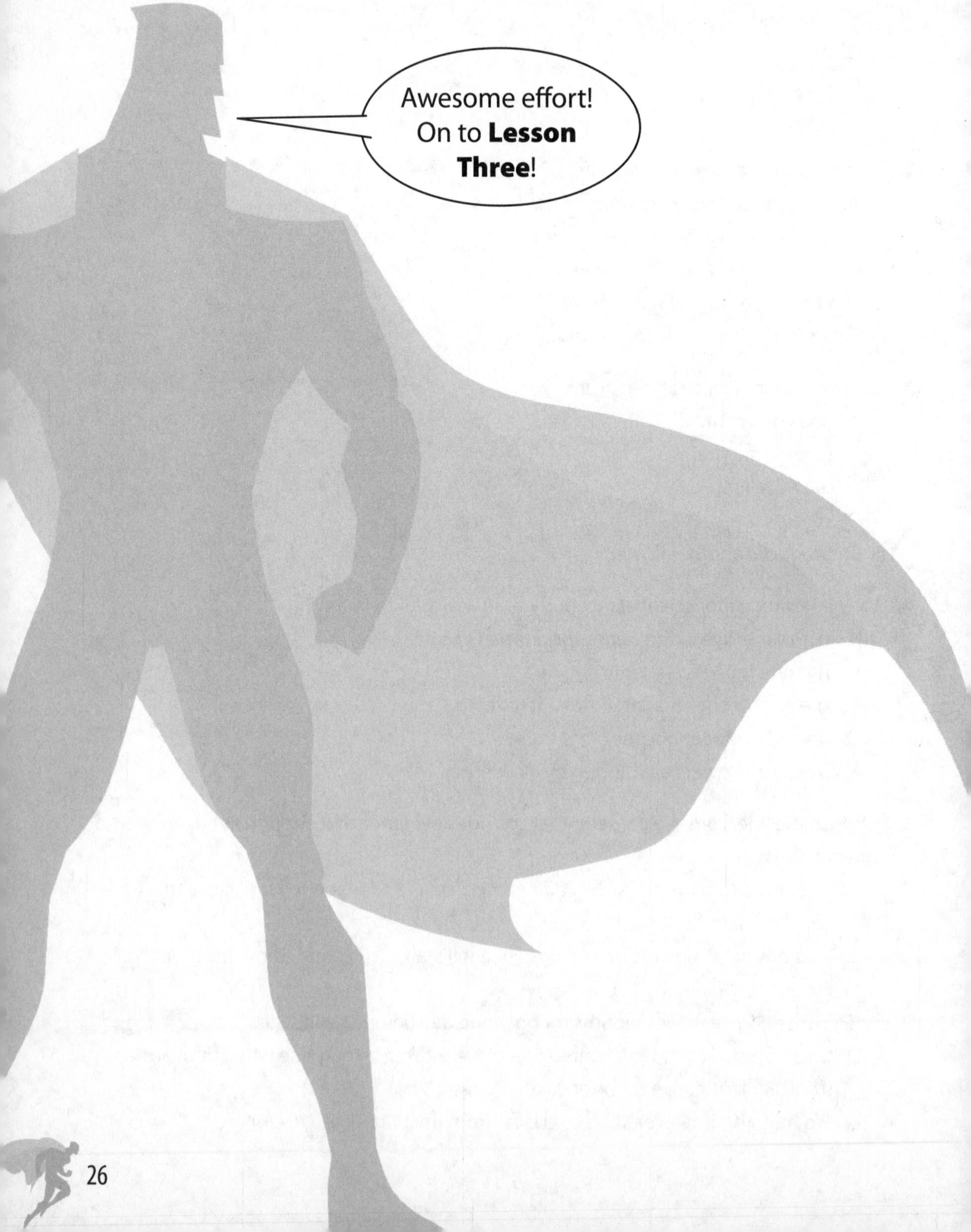
Awesome effort!
On to **Lesson Three**!

Lesson Three

clash
KLASH

v. to have a conflict or disagreement
Maggie and Bill often *clash* over who gets to sit in the front seat of the car.
syn: fight; dispute   *ant: agree*

contradict
KAHN-TRAH-**DIKT**

v. to claim the opposite of; to declare untrue
Allison's choice to stay inside today *contradicts* her usual love of the outdoors.
syn: oppose   *ant: support; agree*

destiny
DES-TIH-NEE

n. the course of future events
Mrs. Stone likes to call teaching her *destiny*; she has never wanted a different career.
syn: fate; fortune

envy
EN-VEE

1. *v.* to be jealous of
2. *n.* bitter jealousy
1. Erica and Jill *envied* their brother, who was allowed to have two popsicles.
2. When Chad received the latest smartphone on his birthday, Brianna felt *envy* toward him.
syn: 1. desire

ignorance
IG-NUH-RENS

n. lack of knowledge or information
Beverly's rude comments showed her *ignorance* of how to make friends.
syn: stupidity   *ant: wisdom; intelligence*

regal
REE-GULL

adj. relating to royalty
The crown on Sir Emony's head made him look especially *regal*.
syn: majestic; noble   *ant: common; plain*

rigid
RIH-JID

adj. not easily bent or changed
Frozen solid, the jump rope was now cold and *rigid*.
syn: stiff; inflexible   *ant: elastic; soft*

sensation
SEN-**SAY**-SHUN

n. something perceived through the senses
I love the *sensation* of walking into an air-conditioned room on a hot day.
syn: feeling

substantial
SUB-**STAN**-CHULL

adj. of a large size, amount, or value
Building the statue in the middle of town called for a *substantial* number of workers.
syn: considerable; significant   ant: unimportant; insignificant

tolerate
TOL-ER-AYT

v. to put up with something
We do not *tolerate* hitting, kicking, or spitting in this classroom.
syn: permit; withstand   ant: ban; prohibit

Exercise I – Words in Context

Using the list of vocabulary words, supply the correct word to complete each sentence.

1. _____ about any topic can be overcome through reading about it.

2. Quinn's apartment doesn't allow pets, so he _____ his cousins, who have both dogs and cats and lots of space for them to roam.

3. Some people enjoy the _____ of being tickled, but I do not.

4. The long metal rod looked _____, but the muscular man bent it like it was plastic.

5. Mastering kung fu calls for a[n] _____ level of patience.

6. My ability to read quickly _____ with your need to read slowly.

7. My mom does not _____ disrespect, so I have to be careful about what I say around her.

8. I want to visit the castle so that I can see how _____ it is.

9. I will _____ Principal Faust's rule against eating in class and give you each one piece of candy.

10. Floyd believed it was _____ that he and his best friend, Alex, lived next door to each other.

Exercise II – Finish the Sentence

First, choose the ending for each sentence that makes the best sense with the italicized vocabulary word used. Then, write your own ending for each sentence that shows you understand the meaning of the vocabulary word.

1. Even though the prosecutor had *substantial* evidence against the robber,…
   A. the judge was still not convinced.
   B. the jury concluded that he was guilty.

2. If Alexis acts like she is *regal*, she probably…
   A. wants to be the princess in the play.
   B. likes to give money to charity.

3. The seat was hard and *rigid*, so…
   A. Megan called someone to repair it.
   B. Dad handed me a pillow.

4. Greg revealed his *ignorance* about music when…
   A. he could not name a single popular song.
   B. he listed each year's #1 hit song from memory.

5. After experiencing the *sensation* of riding a horse for the first time, Leo…
   A. was excited to do it again.
   B. decided that he liked horses.

6. Dustin feels *envy* toward his friend because…
   A. she got a gold star in class, but he did not.
   B. she helped him build a sandcastle.

7. The employees' *destinies* depended on whether the company…
   A. talked to them about pay raises.
   B. decided to shut down.

8. Although Amber *tolerated* the yapping dog, she…
   A. did not know what she could feed it.
   B. did not show much affection for it.

9. The team captains *clashed* when…

    A. the game was over.

    B. they argued about a foul.

10. Kevin's mom and dad *contradicted* each other, so…

    A. Kevin became confused.

    B. Kevin felt relieved.

Exercise III – Crossword Puzzle

Use the clues and the words from this lesson to complete the crossword puzzle.

Across

1. The _____ of the poor, tiny island changed overnight with the discovery of gold.

3. The hypnotist made my arm _____, and I couldn't bend it.

8. Visitors to the castle were treated to a[n] _____ reception, including live music and a ten-course dinner.

9. If you _____ what I say, you had better have a good reason for doing so.

10. Jason wants people to _____ him for his sports car, so he parks it where everyone can see it.

Down

2. Before the field trip, Nate's parents told him to guard his wallet because he was carrying a[n] _____ amount of money, not just some pocket change.

4. In the sixteenth century, people's _____ about medicine and germs led them to blame evil spirits for diseases.

5. Wendell cannot _____ the heat of the desert, so he moved north to Canada.

6. I felt no _____ in my mouth or on my tongue for an hour after the dentist filled the cavity.

7. Patrick wanted to wear his favorite shirt, but his sister said it would _____ with his pants.

Exercise IV – Improving Paragraphs

Carefully read the passage and then choose the best answer for each of the questions. The questions will ask you to make changes to improve the writing of the passage.

1   Everyone knows that dogs need food, water, attention, and exercise. It is difficult to imagine a time when people did not realize the importance of walking their dogs. We can thank Jim Buck for making dog walking a common activity.

2   Born in Manhattan in 1931, Jim Buck spent his childhood showing dogs and training his uncle's horses in Connecticut. He could have followed in his wealthy family's footsteps and joined the steel and shipping business, but he continued working with animals instead. He called his work his "birthright." The job was his **destiny**.

3   **{1}** Jim Buck's School for Dogs opened in 1964, and Jim Buck's School is considered the first dog-walking business in the United States. By the end of that year, the business made $500 per week, a **substantial** amount of money for that time. It would equal about $4,000 a week in today's money. At the company's peak, it employed two dozen people and walked more than 150 dogs a day.

4   For forty years, Mr. Buck could be seen strolling the New York City streets with at least half a dozen, or about 500 pounds, of leashed dogs with him. **{2}** <u>Some referred to him "the grandmaster of New York dog walkers."</u> Though no one seemed to express **envy** at being responsible for so many animals, people did point out Mr. Buck's elegant clothes. He wore tailored suits and expensive dress shoes that clearly **clashed** with the hands-on work he did. Because of his appearance, he became one of the most recognizable people in New York City.

5   [1] Mr. Buck was as loyal to his business as a dog is to its owner. [2] His clients knew that he cared about animals. [3] He took the dogs out on the town in every temperature and weather forecast. [4] He understood that dogs were family members and not just burglar alarms. [5] He walked his clients' dogs no matter the weather, in sunshine or in the midst of a storm. [6] He even owned three dogs himself. **{3}**

6   Buck held his employees to high standards and had **rigid** opinions about what it took to be a great dog walker. In fact, when people applied to work for him, he chose specific canines to test them, including an otter hound that the school staff jokingly nicknamed "Oliver the Awful." Oliver was smart enough to know exactly when he was meant to be testing a walker. During these walks, Oliver was known to run inside phone booths and get himself stuck. Mr. Buck knew that Oliver could teach the potential walkers about how to be gentle with dogs. Trying to pull or lift Oliver out of the phone booth would never work, so the walker had to remain calm and kindly encourage Oliver to come out.

7   Though Jim Buck retired his leash around the year 2000 and died in 2013, his love for dogs and his drive to do the best job possible lives on in many of his former employees, some of whom still walk dogs today. **{4}{5}**

Exercise IV – Improving Paragraphs Questions

1. Which choice shows the best way to separate this sentence into two sentences?

   "Jim Buck's School for Dogs opened in 1964, and Jim Buck's School is considered the first dog-walking business in the United States."

   A. Jim Buck's School for Dogs opened in 1964. It is considered the first dog-walking business in the United States.
   B. Jim Buck's School for Dogs opened in 1964. Considered the first dog-walking business in the United States.
   C. Jim Buck's School for Dogs opened in 1964. Jim Buck's School for Dogs, which opened in 1964, is considered the first dog-walking business in the United States.
   D. Jim Buck's School for Dogs. It opened in 1964, and Jim Buck's School is considered the first dog-walking business in the United States.

2. The underlined sentence needs to be revised. Choose the best revision of the sentence.

   "Some referred to him 'the grandmaster of New York dog walkers.' "

   A. Some referred him "the grandmaster of New York dog walkers."
   B. Some referred to him "the grandmaster of all New York dog walkers."
   C. Some referred to him "grandmaster of New York dog walkers."
   D. Some referred to him as "the grandmaster of New York dog walkers."

3. One sentence in paragraph 5 is not necessary and should be deleted. Choose which sentence to delete.
   A. sentence 1
   B. sentence 2
   C. sentence 3
   D. sentence 4

4. The writer wants to talk about the people who worked for Jim Buck. Choose the best paragraph in which to include those details.
   A. paragraph 1
   B. paragraph 2
   C. paragraph 4
   D. paragraph 6

5. The writer would like to include the following sentence in the passage:

"As a child, Jim loved caring for animals."

Choose the paragraph in which this sentence should be placed.

A. paragraph 1
B. paragraph 2
C. paragraph 3
D. paragraph 4

Review: Lessons 1-3

Exercise I – Related Words

Choose the word that best completes the sentence.

1. The most *vicious* wolf in the pack would also probably be the most _____ one.
   A. dominant
   B. improper
   C. rigid
   D. substantial
   E. inferior

2. Tracy found herself in a[n] _____ with Max because she *contradicted* his opinion of football.
   A. emblem
   B. tragedy
   C. quarrel
   D. sensation
   E. custom

3. I *resented* Kyle for winning the fashion show when his suit _____ with his tie.
   A. contradicted
   B. deceived
   C. magnified
   D. clashed
   E. lingered

4. "Do you *envy* Sally because your grades are _____ to hers?" asked Lena.
   A. substantial
   B. regal
   C. inferior
   D. improper
   E. artificial

5. I cannot _____ Corey's bad attitude, so I'm *severing* all contact with him.
  A. resent
  B. linger
  C. seize
  D. magnify
  E. tolerate

6. The diamond crown is the queen's most treasured *regal* _____.
  A. fragrance
  B. emblem
  C. sensation
  D. idol
  E. custom

7. In my culture, it is a *custom* to appear tense, almost _____, when talking to older people.
  A. inferior
  B. vicious
  C. dominant
  D. rigid
  E. artificial

8. Your _____ about history explains your *improper* behavior during our visit to the Civil War battlefield memorial.
  A. tragedy
  B. ignorance
  C. envy
  D. quarrel
  E. destiny

Exercise II – Synonyms and Antonyms

Match the word with its synonym.

1. _____ seize

A. unnatural

2. _____ improper

B. fruitful

3. _____ tolerate

C. grab

4. _____ artificial

D. divide

5. _____ dominant

E. unsuitable

6. _____ sever

F. commanding

7. _____ fertile

G. withstand

Match the word with its antonym.

8. _____ vicious

H. common

9. _____ ignorance

I. lessen

10. _____ regal

J. actual

11. _____ magnify

K. support

12. _____ contradict

L. gentle

13. _____ abstract

M. leave

14. _____ linger

N. wisdom

Excellent work! On to **Lesson Four**!

Lesson Four

acquaint
UH-**KWAYNT**

v. to make familiar with or be aware of
When my parents were young, they became *acquainted* with the Beatles' music.
syn: know

betray
BEE-**TRAY**

v. to be disloyal or unfaithful to
Please keep the surprise party a secret, and do not *betray* my trust.
syn: deceive

chronological
KRAH-NUH-**LAH**-JIK-ULL

adj. arranged in a time order
Mom arranged our home videos in *chronological* order, starting with one from when I was a baby and ending with a clip from last week.

dispute
DIS-**PYOOT**

n. an argument or debate
My friends like to settle *disputes* by playing "Rock, Paper, Scissors."
syn: quarrel; conflict   ant: agreement

federal
FED-EH-RIL

adj. pertaining to the central, uniting government
Federal laws control how we must take care of the environment.
syn: national   ant: local; state

feeble
FEE-BULL

adj. weak
The *feeble* baby bird had a broken wing, so my mother nursed him back to health.
syn: frail; fragile   ant: strong; durable

govern
GUH-VURN

v. to rule or lead by authority
Elvira *governs* her family farm and its tree nursery.
syn: manage

longitude
LONJ-IH-TOOD

n. the measure of distance east or west across Earth's surface
Mrs. Knowles traces the lines going up and down on the globe to show us *longitude*.

mope
MOHP

v. to be gloomy and disheartened
My sister did nothing but *mope* when her birthday party was canceled.
syn: brood; sulk   *ant: delight; enjoy*

vanity
VAN-IH-TEE

n. too much pride in oneself
The princess likes to stare at herself in the mirror, an act that shows great *vanity*.
syn: arrogance; conceit   *ant: humility; modesty*

Exercise I – Words in Context

Using the list of vocabulary words, supply the correct word to complete each sentence.

1. Mom and Dad had a[n] _____ over where to go for dinner that night; Dad wanted pizza, and Mom wanted sushi.

2. "I am definitely the cutest girl in school!" said Regina, with too much _____.

3. I will often help the _____ old lady down the street bring in her groceries.

4. The cousins stood in line in _____ order, with the youngest child first and the oldest last.

5. By examining the meteor's position in space, scientists determined the _____ at which it would hit Earth.

6. Going to camp provides a way for kids to _____ themselves with other kids.

7. Morgan _____ Jose's trust when she told her closest friends that he still sucked his thumb.

8. If you work for the _____ government, do you get to meet the president?

9. The rule of raising your hand before you speak _____ class discussion.

10. No matter how much you _____ around the house, I am still not letting you go to the party.

Exercise II – Finish the Sentence

First, choose the ending for each sentence that makes the best sense with the italicized vocabulary word used. Then, write your own ending for each sentence that shows you understand the meaning of the vocabulary word.

1. Because my uncle did not tell the story in *chronological* order, I…
   A. could not tell which event came first.
   B. did not believe anything he said.

2. Using *federal* land without permission…
   A. would cause the government to take action.
   B. might upset the school principal.

3. The panda looked so *feeble* that…
   A. the jungle explorer feared it.
   B. the veterinarian wondered if it would survive.

4. When the captain could not determine the ship's *longitude*,…
   A. he pulled out a map to check for landmarks.
   B. he asked me to be his first mate.

5. Joe and Marissa often had *disputes* over…
   A. the distance to the nearest post office.
   B. which school their children should attend.

6. Ryan was known for his *vanity* because…
   A. he volunteered at an animal shelter.
   B. he posted selfies online every day.

7. The substitute teacher tried to *govern* the class, but…
   A. none of the students listened to him.
   B. the students were great listeners.

8. After moving to a new city, Jess took a few weeks to *acquaint* herself with…
   A. a job so that she could rent an apartment.
   B. the couple who lived next door.

9. Justin spent the weekend *moping* after…

    A. his best friend moved away.

    B. it snowed all day on Friday.

10. During the war, the soldier had *betrayed* his country, so…

    A. he received a medal of honor.

    B. his name became a hated word.

Exercise III – Crossword Puzzle

Use the clues and the words from this lesson to complete the crossword puzzle.

Across

4. "That's a pretty _____ excuse for lateness, and I don't believe it," said the teacher.

6. A new fence caused a[n] _____ between the two neighbors over the location of the property line.

8. During the first day of classes, you need to _____ yourself with the rules.

9. Put all the pictures you took in _____ order so we can see how the family has grown.

10. Alex _____ me even though I had always been a loyal friend.

Down

1. Evan doesn't hide his _____, and his high opinion of himself makes people dislike him.

2. The _____ agents started hunting for someone who had started forest fires in multiple states.

3. You're not old enough to take care of a parrot; that's my decision, so don't _____ about it all week!

5. At our _____ , it's 2:00 pm, but in England, 3,500 miles away, it is 7:00 pm.

7. Captain Smith was chosen to _____ the colony because he had experience surviving in the wild.

Exercise IV – Critical Reading

Carefully read the passage and then choose the best answer for each of the questions that follow. The passage contains vocabulary words from the lesson.

You have probably heard of Benedict Arnold. He was the American general who **betrayed** his country during the American War of Independence. You might not have heard, however, that he wasn't working alone. Historians believe his wife, Peggy Shippen, might have been the mastermind.

5   Benedict Arnold and Peggy Shippen had something of a strange love story. Peggy belonged to a powerful family in Philadelphia. The family was loyal to Britain. She became **acquainted** with Benedict when the Continental Army took over Philadelphia. This was the army that he **governed**. Even though they were on opposite sides of the **dispute** between England and the American colonies, Peggy and
10   Benedict began a romantic relationship in 1778. They were married in 1779.

    Long before Peggy met Benedict, she had become friends with a British Army officer named John André. When Peggy was young, and the British army still occupied Philadelphia, her family would host social gatherings. She met John André at that time. Her relationship with him would become very important to Benedict
15   Arnold's plan.

    Shortly after Benedict married Peggy, he had a conflict with the council that managed Pennsylvania. They accused him of crimes related to his poor handling of **federal** money. He angrily quit his position. However, he had large debts for his fancy home. Having lost faith in the cause he had fought for, Arnold offered help to
20   the British in return for money and power. Peggy passed letters between Benedict Arnold and John André during women's meetings she attended. Historians believe the idea might have been Peggy's because she, not Benedict, was John's friend. Benedict and John wrote covert messages in a code only they knew or with invisible ink. The letters contained details about the plans, locations, and supplies of American troops.

25   Benedict Arnold pretended to be loyal to the cause of American independence. He became the commander of West Point, an important fort in New York. Using his power as commander, he slowly weakened the defenses around West Point and sent troops to less important locations. He also reported American troop movements to John André. Finally, Benedict offered to surrender West Point to the British in return
30   for 20,000 pounds (about 1 million dollars today).

    Soldiers ended Arnold's plan when they captured John André and his letters from Arnold. André was executed as a spy. General George Washington realized Arnold, too, was guilty and should be arrested. When the general confronted Peggy with the news about Benedict, she seemed to have gone insane. Her panic convinced
35   Washington that she had nothing to do with her husband's plans. Peggy was not, however, a **feeble** woman. Most likely, she acted that way to trick Washington. Doing so would give Benedict more time to escape to New York City.

Exercise IV – Critical Reading Questions

1. As used on line 23, the word *covert* means
   A. remembered.
   B. received.
   C. important.
   D. secret.
   E. complicated.

2. Which words from the passage best support your choice for Question 1?
   A. code, invisible
   B. betrayed, mastermind
   C. conflict, crimes
   D. dispute, romantic
   E. details, pretended

3. From the passage, which fact can you conclude about the history of Philadelphia?
   A. It was the capital of the American colonies.
   B. Peggy's family hosted the most popular events in the city.
   C. Both the British and the American armies occupied the city at some point.
   D. Philadelphia was not far from New York.
   E. Peggy Shippen was secretly spying for the Americans.

4. The author suggests that Peggy's reaction to her husband's crime was
   A. odd.
   B. foolish.
   C. frightening.
   D. appropriate.
   E. false.

5. Choose the part of the passage that best supports your answer to the previous question.
   A. "André was executed as a spy." (line 32)
   B. "General George Washington realized Arnold, too, was guilty, and should be arrested." (lines 32-33)
   C. "Her panic convinced Washington that she had nothing to do with her husband's plans." (lines 34-35)
   D. "Most likely, she acted that way to trick Washington." (line 36)
   E. "Doing so would give Benedict more time to escape to New York City." (lines 36-37)

Superior effort! On to **Lesson Five**!

Lesson Five

decay
DEH-**KAY**

v. to rot away or break down
By the week after Halloween, all the jack-o'-lanterns outside were starting to *decay*.
syn: decompose   *ant: develop; grow*

dissatisfied
DIS-**SA**-TIS-FYD

adj. feeling displeasure; not contented
The restaurant manager gives refunds to *dissatisfied* customers.
syn: disappointed   *ant: pleased; content*

distinguished
DIS-**TING**-WISHD

adj. noble, dignified, and respected
At the ceremony, Mark's perfect attendance award marked him as a *distinguished* student.
syn: famous; renowned   *ant: unknown*

emigrate
EH-MIH-GRAYT

v. to leave one's country to settle in another
Many people want to *emigrate* from their own countries and live in the United States.
syn: depart; migrate   *ant: stay; remain*

facility
FAH-**SIL**-IH-TEE

n. a building that serves a certain purpose
I take ballet lessons at a dance *facility* on 44th Street.
syn: establishment; institute

foe
FOH

n. a personal enemy or rival
Grandpa Kenny finally defeated his long-time *foe* in a game of checkers.
syn: opponent; contender   *ant: ally; friend*

frigid
FRIH-JID

adj. very cold
This winter produced record-breaking *frigid* weather, with temperatures far below zero.
syn: freezing   *ant: warm; hot*

heirloom
AYR-LOOM

n. a valued object passed down from one generation to the next

This ring is a family *heirloom*; my grandmother wore it, my mother wore it, and now, I wear it.

syn: inheritance

postpone
POHST-**POHN**

v. to put off doing until later

Until we can find a new pilot, we must *postpone* this flight.

syn: delay   *ant: begin; start*

timid
TIH-MID

adj. lacking confidence and courage

Francesca used to be a *timid* girl, but now, she loves to chat with everyone.

syn: shy; afraid   *ant: confident*

Exercise I – Words in Context

Using the list of vocabulary words, supply the correct word to complete each sentence.

1. "Our new student _____ here all the way from Australia!" said Mr. Erikson.

2. I am sorry that you were _____ with dinner; next time, I will try to make something you like.

3. If you leave meat out in the heat, it will quickly _____.

4. The carnival will be _____ until we no longer have a tornado watch.

5. In the season finale of *Super Dudes*, Mr. Mighty fought a battle against his greatest _____.

6. The post office is a[n] _____ that sorts and delivers mail for the entire town.

7. Paulette is so _____ that it took her almost three months to speak in class.

8. Before the weather becomes too _____, bears usually find a warm cave to hibernate in.

9. Twenty years of teaching earned Mrs. Levine the title of "_____ Educator."

10. The house we live in is a[n] _____ that our family has owned for over 200 years.

Exercise II – Finish the Sentence

First, choose the ending for each sentence that makes the best sense with the italicized vocabulary word used. Then, write your own ending for each sentence that shows you understand the meaning of the vocabulary word.

1. When Sasha brought the *timid* cat home, it…
    A. hid under the sofa.
    B. hissed at everyone.

2. While working in *frigid* Antarctic temperatures, scientists…
    A. wore many layers of clothing.
    B. discovered a new kind of penguin.

3. If a customer is *dissatisfied*, the manager will first…
    A. ask the customer to leave.
    B. apologize to the customer.

4. Since Brandon is a *distinguished* piano player,…
    A. he was invited to perform at Carnegie Hall.
    B. he took lessons to improve.

5. The recycling *facility*…
    A. came with instructions.
    B. took up the whole block.

6. Laura's locket was an *heirloom* that…
    A. her grandparents had given her.
    B. was brand-new and shiny.

7. When Harry faced his main *foe* during the baseball game,…
    A. he pitched the same way he usually did.
    B. he seemed extra motivated to win.

8. The city *postponed* the fireworks because…
    A. of a worrisome hurricane alert.
    B. it was time to celebrate Independence Day.

9. As the garbage *decayed* in the empty lot,…

    A. Amy wondered who had littered.

    B. a disgusting smell filled the air.

10. Jin's family *emigrated* from China to the United States in order to…

    A. have access to the US education system.

    B. visit their relatives in Hong Kong.

Exercise III – Crossword Puzzle

Use the clues and the words from this lesson to complete the crossword puzzle.

Across

2. "Ms. Gordon, could we please _____ the test until Monday?" begged Mylie.

5. They finally began building the athletic _____ next to the new field.

6. After Jann _____ from Norway, it took him a few months to adapt to living in Mississippi.

8. Val was completely _____ that he didn't get an *A* on his book report.

9. The pocket watch is a[n] _____ that my great-grandparents brought with them from Russia in 1880.

Down

1. Tom's athletic abilities _____ as he grew older.

3. The _____ baby gorilla hung on to his mother for a few months before finally letting go.

4. The elderly veteran is a[n] _____ member of the community.

5. Even after the electricity went off, meat in the most _____ part of the freezer didn't thaw out.

7. Mayor Bill's _____, Mrs. Henderson, attended every town meeting so she could complain about Bill's decisions.

Exercise IV – Critical Reading

Carefully read the passage and then choose the best answer for each of the questions that follow. The passage contains vocabulary words from the lesson.

Early every morning, ten-year-old Aya walks down a dusty road past hundreds of canvas tents to go to school. Aya lives in a refugee camp. She and her family **emigrated** from their homeland, Syria, in order to escape a civil war. They crossed the border into Jordan with few effects—just some clothes, basic supplies, and small
5   **heirlooms** to remind themselves of their family still in Syria. Her parents hope to return one day. But they question when it will be safe to do so. For now, they know that education is the only way to provide their daughter with a promising future.

Classrooms in Jordan are overcrowded, so Aya cannot attend a local school. Instead, she goes to one of the tiny, rough education **facilities** in Zaatari refugee
10   camp. The school depends on donations from Middle Eastern governments and international aid organizations. Resources are very limited. Each school has one classroom, a chalkboard, and a dozen wooden tables. Classes occur in shifts. The girls receive three hours of lessons in the morning. Then, they leave so the boys can attend class for three hours in the afternoon.

15   The local teachers who volunteer at Zaatari camp work hard to create a place where students feel safe. Many of the children are **timid** because they have seen the horrors of war in Syria. When planes fly overhead, one of Aya's classmates jumps from her chair and hides in the corner. Her home in Syria had been bombed. The roar of the aircraft reminds her of the destruction. Aya's teacher stops the lesson to
20   reassure the girl that she is all right.

Given the limited money, short school days, and stressful classroom conditions, you might expect Aya to feel **dissatisfied** with her educational experiences. But she is grateful to have an opportunity to learn. One in every three children at Zaatari does not attend school. Some have **postponed** their studies until they can return to Syria.
25   Many of them must work in order to help support their families. Aya may not have much, but she is one of the lucky children in Zaatari.

Exercise IV – Critical Reading Questions

1. The primary purpose of this passage is to
   A. describe what schools are like in refugee camps.
   B. depict one girl's struggle to get an education.
   C. explain why school is important to refugees.
   D. reveal how all Syrians are affected by war.
   E. encourage readers to take a side in the war.

2. As used in line 4, *effects* most nearly means
   A. arguments.
   B. happenings.
   C. belongings.
   D. problems.
   E. feelings.

3. Classes are most likely set up in shifts because
   A. children feel safe in small groups.
   B. all the students cannot fit in the schools at once.
   C. girls and boys learn different subjects.
   D. children are too busy for full school days.
   E. teachers also work at Jordanian schools.

4. Choose the line that best supports your answer to the previous question.
   A. "Classrooms in Jordan are overcrowded, so Aya cannot attend a local school." (line 8)
   B. "The school depends on donations from Middle Eastern governments and international aid organizations." (lines 10-11)
   C. "Resources are very limited." (line 11)
   D. "Many of the children are timid because they have seen the horrors of war in Syria." (lines 16-17)
   E. "Each school has one classroom, a chalkboard, and a dozen wooden tables." (lines 11-12)

5. Most of the children who do not attend school decided not to because
   A. they want to go to school in Syria.
   B. the local Jordanian schools have no room.
   C. they do not feel safe there.
   D. they need to earn money.
   E. the lessons are too short to be worthwhile.

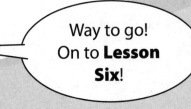

Vocabulary
Power Plus
Vocabulary, Reading, and
Writing Exercises

5 LEVEL

Lesson Six

abandon
AH-**BAN**-DUN

v. to leave behind; to give up completely
Do not *abandon* me when we enter the haunted house; it is too scary to wander through alone.
syn: desert   *ant: keep*

carnivore
KAR-NIH-VOR

n. an animal that eats mainly meat
Cheetahs are *carnivores* that eat other animals, such as gazelles.
                    ant: herbivore

climate
KLIY-MIT

n. the long-term weather conditions of an area
The *climate* of the Amazon Rainforest is hot and humid year-round.
syn: environment

elementary
EL-EH-**MEN**-TREE

adj. basic; not difficult
Adding and subtracting numbers seems like *elementary* math now that we know how to divide and multiply.
syn: fundamental; simple   *ant: advanced; complex*

exterminate
EX-**TUR**-MIH-NAYT

v. to destroy completely; to kill all
Using traps and poison, it took us six weeks to *exterminate* the rats in the basement.
syn: eliminate; destroy   *ant: create; preserve*

inauguration
IN-AWG-YUH-**RAY**-SHUN

n. a ceremony in which someone is formally sworn into office
We had a small party after the *inauguration* of our new scout leader.
syn: swearing-in

mellow
MEL-OH

adj. gentle and pleasant
My puppy has a *mellow* personality that makes me love her even more than when I first brought her home.
syn: relaxed; calm   *ant: harsh; irritated*

55

revolt

REH-**VOLT**

v. to rise up and fight those in power

Justin *revolted* against his boss's rude behavior and quit his job as a waiter on a busy night.

syn: rebel; defy   *ant: submit; surrender*

urban

UR-BIN

adj. relating to city life, as opposed to country life

Ginger left the lights and sounds of her *urban* neighborhood to visit her grandparents in the country.

ant: rural; country

verdict

VUR-DIKT

n. an official decision

After much debate, the jury has a final *verdict*: Donald is innocent.

syn: judgment; opinion

Exercise I – Words in Context

Using the list of vocabulary words, supply the correct word to complete each sentence.

1. Be _____ and enjoy the sunshine; it's supposed to rain later.

2. Penguins need to live in a cold _____ in order to survive.

3. People can understand a foreign language before they can speak it because listening is a more _____ skill than talking.

4. The judges on the show came to a[n] _____ and announced the winner.

5. The angry mob _____ against the evil king, grabbing pitchforks and swords to fight him.

6. Mr. Minnate _____ the cockroaches that were hiding around our house.

7. The president of the United States beamed with pride at his official _____.

8. Kyle's family jokes that he is like a[n] _____ because he gobbles meat like a lion does.

9. Benjamin's team travels to New York City, Boston, and other _____ areas.

10. I almost _____ my plans to eat healthier when I saw the dessert menu.

Exercise II – Finish the Sentence

First, choose the ending for each sentence that makes the best sense with the italicized vocabulary word used. Then, write your own ending for each sentence that shows you understand the meaning of the vocabulary word.

1. The dolphin had to practice the *elementary* tricks…
   A. so it could begin its training.
   B. before it could learn advanced ones.

2. Once the field trip bus got out of the *urban* area,…
   A. we passed fewer farms.
   B. we could no longer see skyscrapers.

3. Usually, the giraffe area at the zoo is fairly *mellow*, but today,…
   A. one giraffe destroyed its pen.
   B. the animals behaved calmly.

4. If the *climate* in Arizona changes…
   A. we should delay our trip for a week.
   B. we might decide not to move there.

5. We all wore formal clothing to the party after the *inauguration* because…
   A. we wanted to impress our new governor.
   B. the bride and groom insisted that we do.

6. Grizzly bears aren't complete *carnivores* because they…
   A. also eat vegetables.
   B. do not ever eat meat.

7. Our town came to a *verdict* about…
   A. how far a mile should be.
   B. where to build the new school.

8. The movie's villain tried to *exterminate* all the…
   A. ways to take over the world.
   B. people who stood in his way.

9. Many people in history have *revolted* against their leaders when…

    A. those leaders did terrible things.

    B. those leaders promised equality.

10. The explorers *abandoned* their journey after…

    A. a traveler warned them of dangers ahead.

    B. their last member finished preparing her pack.

Exercise III – Crossword Puzzle

Use the clues and the words from this lesson to complete the crossword puzzle.

Across

1. The state gardens built a room with a dry, artificial _____ just for cacti.

3. The coach had the team perform some _____ exercises before moving on to more advanced techniques.

7. Farmer Hut uses pesticides to _____ the bugs that eat his crops.

9. *Tyrannosaurus rex* was the greatest _____ in the prehistoric world; it had 9-inch-long teeth.

10. The _____ is in, and Lilly is the winner of the talent show.

Down

2. The newly elected prime minister will accept her duties during her _____.

4. The _____ music playing in the background was very soothing.

5. The _____ softball league includes teams from all districts of the city.

6. The hyena wouldn't _____ its meal until a hungry lion approached.

8. Some people wanted to _____ when the government imposed a huge tax on gasoline.

Exercise IV – Improving Paragraphs

Carefully read the passage and then choose the best answer for each of the questions.
The questions will ask you to make changes to improve the writing of the passage.

1   A secret world lies beneath the streets of Paris, France. It is called the Paris catacombs. Miles of centuries-old <u>tunnels, they twist</u> **{1}** sixty-five feet below the city's historic buildings and cobblestone roads. Some sections of the catacombs were used for mining. Others served as the final resting places for millions of Paris's citizens. Inside these dark corridors, the sad tale of Philibert Aspairt unfolded.

2   **{2}** [1] One night, Aspairt **abandoned** his post at the hospital's gateway and snuck into the catacombs in search of a secret storage cellar owned by a group of Parisian monks. [2] At the time, the catacombs were easily accessible throughout Paris. [3] One of the entrances was right inside the Val-de-Grâce hospital. [4] Aspairt ventured into the maze with only a single lantern to light his way. [5] Although he knew the city's streets well, Aspairt was unfamiliar with the winding pathways of the catacombs. [6] The dim candlelight flickered as Aspairt journeyed deeper and deeper into the tunnels. [7] The skeleton wore tattered clothing and its bony fingers held a set of keys and a small lantern. [8] Then, before Aspairt could find the secret cellar or figure out where he was, the lantern went out. [9] The doorman wandered in the blackness for what must have seemed like ages. **{3}**

3   Back at Val-de-Grâce hospital, people noticed Aspairt was missing. For days, no one could find him. Search efforts were weak because many people in the city had **revolted** against the French government at the time. No one thought to look in the catacombs. Most people believed Aspairt ran away from Paris without telling anyone. The official search for Aspairt soon ended, forgotten amid the chaos of the revolution.

4   Eleven years later, in 1804, mining inspectors were startled to discover a shocking sight. There was a skeleton leaning against one of the stone walls! Inspectors examined the **{4}** <u>keys, were well preserved</u> by the tunnel's chilly **climate**. One of the men recognized the keys as those belonging to Val-de-Grâce hospital. After much debate among the mining inspectors, the **verdict** was clear: They had finally found Philibert Aspairt.

5   [1] Aspairt was buried not far from where his skeleton was recovered. [2] Nobody knew where Aspairt was for almost twelve years. [3] A tombstone placed near Aspairt's grave tells his unlucky story. [4] It also serves as a warning to those who might wish to explore the underground tunnels on their own. [5] Today, his grave is a famous destination for **urban** explorers who enjoy seeing little-known parts of the city. [6] Adventurers should beware, however; entering the Paris catacombs is illegal and extremely dangerous. [7] Sometimes it's best to stay above ground because you might get buried early, as Aspairt was. **{5}**

Exercise IV – Improving Paragraphs Questions

1. Choose the best way to fix the underlined part of this sentence:

"Miles of centuries-old <u>tunnels, they twist</u> sixty-five feet below the city's historic buildings and cobblestone roads."

A. tunnels that twist

B. tunnels twist

C. tunnels twisting

D. tunnels twists

2. The writer would like to add a sentence at this point in the passage. Choose the best sentence to use as an introduction to paragraph 2.

A. "People do not realize that getting lost in the catacombs is a common occurrence."

B. "One time, explorers of the underground catacombs found a skeleton up against one of the walls."

C. "The process of mining inspection did not come to be until the early 19th century."

D. "In 1793, Philibert Aspairt was a doorman for Val-de-Grâce hospital located in the center of Paris."

3. One of the sentences in paragraph 2 does not belong there. The sentence should be moved to paragraph 4. Choose the sentence that should be moved to paragraph 4.

A. sentence 1

B. sentence 3

C. sentence 7

D. sentence 9

4. Choose the best way to fix the underlined portion of the sentence below.

"Inspectors examined the <u>keys, were well preserved</u> by the tunnel's chilly climate."

A. keys were well preserved

B. keys, which were well preserved

C. keys, are well preserved

D. keys, they were well preserved

5. One sentence in paragraph 5 is unnecessary. Choose the sentence that can be deleted without hurting the passage.

A. sentence 1

B. sentence 2

C. sentence 3

D. sentence 4

Review: Lessons 4-6

Exercise I – Related Words

Choose the word that best completes the sentence.

1. The emperor decided that the best way to stay in power would be to *exterminate* all his
_____.

    A. carnivores

    B. vanities

    C. disputes

    D. facilities

    E. foes

2. Members of the jury had a *dispute* over the _____—was Fred guilty or not?

    A. verdict

    B. climate

    C. facility

    D. inauguration

    E. vanity

3. Citizens decided to _____ against the evil man who *governed* their country.

    A. abandon

    B. betray

    C. decay

    D. revolt

    E. mope

4. Theo *betrayed* Anna's trust by _____ her in the middle of the party.

    A. revolting

    B. emigrating

    C. acquainting

    D. exterminating

    E. abandoning

5. Tia *emigrated* from a farm town in Mexico to a more _____ area in the United States.

    A. mellow

    B. urban

    C. chronological

    D. dissatisfied

    E. elementary

6. "I know you're *dissatisfied* with your test grade, but that's no reason to _____ around all day," said Dad.

    A. postpone

    B. emigrate

    C. mope

    D. revolt

    E. decay

7. Greg was *timid*, but not _____: He could lift very heavy weights.

    A. frigid

    B. distinguished

    C. mellow

    D. feeble

    E. federal

8. Episode 4 of my favorite show was *postponed* and will be shown after Episode 5, so the series will no longer air in _____ order.

    A. chronological

    B. federal

    C. elementary

    D. urban

    E. frigid

Exercise II – Synonyms and Antonyms

Match the word with its synonym.

1. _____ mope	**A.** desert
2. _____ distinguished	**B.** deceive
3. _____ elementary	**C.** quarrel
4. _____ betray	**D.** sulk
5. _____ abandon	**E.** fundamental
6. _____ verdict	**F.** renowned
7. _____ dispute	**G.** judgment

Match the word with its antonym.

8. _____ feeble	**H.** humility
9. _____ foe	**I.** harsh
10. _____ timid	**J.** rural
11. _____ vanity	**K.** strong
12. _____ frigid	**L.** ally
13. _____ mellow	**M.** confident
14. _____ urban	**N.** warm

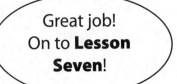

Lesson Seven

amplify
AMP-LIH-FIY

v. to increase in strength, size, or effect

Maybe we could use two speakers to further *amplify* the microphone's sound.

syn: enlarge; expand   *ant: decrease; lessen*

emphasize
EM-FIH-SIYZ

v. to place extra attention on

Meagan underlined the words that she wanted to *emphasize* during her speech.

syn: stress; highlight   *ant: ignore; understate*

extravagant
EX-**TRA**-VIH-GENT

adj. wastefully fancy or excessive

The owner of Sports Unlimited threw an *extravagant* party that cost $250,000.

syn: lavish   *ant: plain*

finance
FIY-NANS

v. to provide or to raise money for

Patty's grandfather was kind enough to *finance* her vacation to Israel.

syn: fund; bankroll

inspire
IN-**SPIY**-ER

v. to motivate through action

The real-life adventures of the explorer *inspired* a whole series of books and movies.

syn: move; affect   *ant: discourage*

majority
MAH-**JOR**-IH-TEE

n. more than half

The *majority* of the class went outside for recess, but a few kids stayed inside.

syn: most   *ant: minority*

nomad
NO-MAD

n. a person who continuously roams from place to place

The busy *nomad* has lived in four different places just this year.

syn: wanderer   *ant: settler*

preliminary
PREE-**LIM**-IH-NEH-REE

adj. relating to the first portion; occurring before the main part

Before we played tag, the gym teacher gave us a *preliminary* talk about the rules.

syn: introductory; initial   ant: concluding; final

radiate
RAY-DEE-AYT

v. to send or move outward from a center

When she won the dance contest, Lilah practically *radiated* with joy.

syn: emit; shine

treacherous
TREH-CHUR-US

adj. dangerous and deceptive

Ascending Mount Everest is *treacherous* even for a well-trained climber; some people die during the trip.

syn: hazardous; difficult   ant: safe; reliable

Exercise I – Words in Context

Using the list of vocabulary words, supply the correct word to complete each sentence.

1. "You must _____ your voice so everyone can hear you," said the director of the play.

2. Before every football game, the school has a[n] _____ pep rally.

3. For my birthday present this year, Grandma will _____ cooking lessons for me.

4. In my family, the _____ rules; we go out to eat wherever most of us want to go.

5. The _____ meal featured eight courses, and the guests used fancy china and silverware.

6. Gretel _____ that reducing our use of oil would help the environment.

7. I was surprised that Jimmy painted a portrait of me; I guess I _____ him.

8. The furnace at the center of the basement _____ a steady heat.

9. A frozen pond can be _____ if the ice is thin in some places.

10. Jesse could never live like a[n] _____; he likes staying in one place.

Exercise II – Finish the Sentence

First, choose the ending for each sentence that makes the best sense with the italicized vocabulary word used. Then, write your own ending for each sentence that shows you understand the meaning of the vocabulary word.

1. During the *preliminary* audition for the school play,…
   A. everyone prepared for the last performance of the show later that evening.
   B. students who could sing well were offered important roles.

2. The *treacherous* roads caused…
   A. the family to stop for dinner.
   B. a nasty car accident.

3. Louisa couldn't accept my *extravagant* present because…
   A. it was too expensive for a friendly gift.
   B. it was not her favorite color.

4. After Kyle had finished the *majority* of his homework,…
   A. he relaxed, knowing that he'd be able to finish the rest on time.
   B. he knew that he would be in trouble for getting so little done.

5. The story about the athlete's determination *inspired* Kate to…
   A. start going to the gym regularly.
   B. attend more sporting events.

6. When Julia was young, her family was forced to live like *nomads* because…
   A. none of them knew how to cook.
   B. they moved from place to place often.

7. Dad has said many times, "Let me *emphasize* to you kids the…
   A. decision to stay up all night."
   B. importance of focusing on school."

8. We had to *finance* the trip because…
   A. our parents wouldn't pay for it.
   B. our flight was delayed.

9. The number of people playing the lottery last week was *amplified* when…

    A. somebody stole the winning money.

    B. the winning pot tripled in size.

10. The quills on the porcupine stuck out and *radiated*…

    A. my finger when I tried to pet it.

    B. a message that they were dangerous.

Exercise III – Crossword Puzzle

Use the clues and the words from this lesson to complete the crossword puzzle.

Across

2. The shock waves from the earthquake _____ out nearly 200 miles from the center.

5. Tyler bought a speaker to _____ the sound of his TV.

7. Prairie dogs, which stay close to their homes, are not _____ that wander all over, like bison.

8. Some people think playing video games is a[n] _____ requirement for getting a job in the computer industry.

10. The _____ of Americans drive cars to work or school, while in other countries, people ride trains or buses.

Down

1. Mom told us to watch out for _____ currents when we went to the beach.

3. Mr. Lukas _____ to us that we needed to end our sentences with the right punctuation mark.

4. Sam started to _____ his college education when he was only eleven by opening a savings account at the bank.

6. There is no need for my car to have _____ features as long as it is safe to drive.

9. What _____ your short story about a lonely alien?

Exercise IV – Critical Reading

Carefully read the passage and then choose the best answer for each of the questions that follow. The passage contains vocabulary words from the lesson.

A person who climbs Mount Everest can become an **inspiration** to anyone who wants to succeed at something. The feat requires peak physical fitness, the strength not to quit, and mountain climbing skills. Reaching the top of the world's tallest mountain is certainly an impressive accomplishment. But people who **emphasize** the
5 skill of those who climb Everest ignore one important fact: Those climbers did not arrive at the top without help. The Sherpa, who are local mountaineers and guides, carry these celebrated climbers' heavy supplies. Climbers may become famous, but, generally, their Sherpa guides do not.

The Sherpa people were originally **nomads** from Tibet, a region in southwestern
10 China. Five hundred years ago, the Sherpa migrated to Nepal, a small country in the Himalayan Mountains between China and India. Having lived in high altitudes for many generations, the Sherpa are used to the thin air, which contains less oxygen than air closer to sea level does. As Everest became a destination for daring tourists, Sherpa found work as guides and assistants for climbers who came from all over the
15 world. It is one of the most dangerous jobs in the world.

Unlike the typical mountaineer who climbs Everest only once or twice, Sherpa guides travel up and down the mountain many times throughout their lives. They make **preliminary** trips up Everest, securing ropes to the rocks and ice so that other climbers can navigate the steep, icy slope with less difficulty and danger. During
20 climbing season, the Sherpa will journey over parts of the mountain multiple times, though they usually will not reach the top more than once a year.

One **treacherous** area the Sherpa cross is the Khumbu Icefall. It is a section of glacier where deep, wide crevasses can form in the ice under climbers' feet, and huge blocks of ice can tumble down the mountainside in avalanches. The **amplified**
25 dangers of the Khumbu Icefall became all too clear in April 2014, when sixteen Sherpa guides died in an avalanche while preparing the route for the spring climbing season. This incident brought attention to the real possibility of injury or death that Sherpa face in order to earn money to support their families.

So the next time you hear about mountain climbers hiking to the top of Mount
30 Everest, remember that they did not make the journey alone. Remember the brave Sherpa who put themselves at risk in order to help others accomplish their dreams of reaching the top of the world.

Exercise IV – Critical Reading Questions

1. The main purpose of this passage is to
    A. describe the culture of the Sherpa in Nepal.
    B. argue that tourist mountaineers are not skilled.
    C. show the geography of Mount Everest.
    D. suggest that Sherpa are underappreciated.
    E. explain the history of explorations of Mount Everest.

2. As used in line 23, the word *crevasses* most nearly means
    A. dangers.
    B. cracks.
    C. canyons.
    D. storms.
    E. cliffs.

3. In 2014, sixteen Sherpa died
    A. when their ropes snapped.
    B. from hypothermia.
    C. during a snowstorm.
    D. from altitude sickness.
    E. in an avalanche.

4. Why are Sherpa at greater risk of injury or death than Western climbers are?
    A. They can't predict avalanches.
    B. They do not use oxygen tanks.
    C. They climb Everest more frequently.
    D. They do not train as much.
    E. They work harder than other mountaineers do.

5. Which portion of the passage best supports your answer to Question 4?
    A. "During climbing season, the Sherpa will journey over parts of the mountain multiple times…" (lines 19-20)
    B. "Having lived in high altitudes for many generations, the Sherpa are used to the thin air…" (lines 11-12)
    C. "The Sherpa, who are all local mountaineers and guides, carry these celebrated climbers' heavy supplies." (lines 6-7)
    D. "They make preliminary trips up Everest, securing ropes to the rocks and ice…" (lines 17-18)
    E. "Climbers may become famous, but, generally, their Sherpa guides do not." (lines 7-8)

Lesson Eight

commodity
KUH-**MAH**-DIH-TEE

n. something that can be bought, sold, or traded
During the California Gold Rush, clothing, tools, and even coffee were valuable *commodities*.
syn: product; good

hectic
HEK-TIK

adj. extremely active or busy; confused
Getting ready for school can be very *hectic* when you wake up late.
syn: hurried   ant: calm

intend
IN-**TEND**

v. to have something in mind as a goal or purpose
I had *intended* to bake a cake, but decided to make cupcakes at the last minute.
syn: plan

invincible
IN-**VINS**-IH-BULL

adj. unable to be defeated or beaten
The rulers thought the castle was *invincible* until the invaders broke through the gate.
syn: indestructible   ant: weak; vulnerable

minority
MIY-**NOR**-IH-TEE

n. less than half
Dogs who do not love to chase cats are in the *minority*.
ant: majority

remark
REE-**MARK**

v. to say
"That movie was absolutely worth the cost of the ticket," Kurt *remarked*.
syn: comment; mention

significant
SIG-**NIH**-FIH-KINT

adj. important
The teacher said we could start a chess club if there was *significant* interest in playing.
syn: notable; noteworthy   ant: unimportant; trivial

site

SIYT

n. a specific place something is located

This old building is the *site* where the famous movie *Sonic Tonsils* was filmed.

syn: location; spot

superstition

SOOP-ER-**STIH**-SHIN

n. a belief based on magic or luck rather than reason

My mother believes the *superstition* that walking under a ladder gives you bad luck.

trespass

TRES-PAS

v. to enter someone's property without permission

The sign said "Do Not Enter," but we *trespassed* anyway.

syn: intrude

Exercise I – Words in Context

Using the list of vocabulary words, supply the correct word to complete each sentence.

1. The boxer had never lost a fight, and fans began to believe he might even be _____.

2. Mike _____ to use his fitness club to teach his classmates how to exercise safely.

3. The most _____ part of the movie is happening in a second, so pay attention.

4. While Janice was in Paris, she visited several historical _____, including the Eiffel Tower.

5. Mr. Jonas was furious when the neighborhood kids _____ on his property.

6. Ocean World Shop's main _____ are bathing suits, flip-flops, and sunscreen.

7. The _____ of some cultures include animals that predict the future.

8. The tour guide _____ to the tourists that the gardens were at least a thousand years old.

9. Only a[n] _____ of children hate the taste of chocolate.

10. With three different graduation parties, this month is sure to be a[n] _____ one!

Exercise II – Finish the Sentence

First, choose the ending for each sentence that makes the best sense with the italicized vocabulary word used. Then, write your own ending for each sentence that shows you understand the meaning of the vocabulary word.

1. The villagers believe in a *superstition* in which…
   A. anyone who says a certain name will be cursed.
   B. only things that can be proven through science are true.

2. What makes high school really *significant* is that…
   A. you have to do homework every single night.
   B. how you do there determines what college you go to.

3. Even though Dash's previous owner had treated him badly, the dog's *invincible* spirit allowed…
   A. him to trust his new family.
   B. his new owner to comfort him.

4. The *hectic* day before moving to a new home became…
   A. a sad one—we had to say goodbye to our old home.
   B. easier once all the boxes were packed.

5. The city decided to restore the *site* because…
   A. the current building was unsafe.
   B. many citizens protested the law.

6. To get the *commodities* to customers in time, the store had to…
   A. call them about the discounts.
   B. conduct a rush delivery.

7. Although only a *minority* of students wanted bottled water in the cafeteria,…
   A. the school board agreed with them.
   B. none of the teachers did either.

8. Because I *remarked* that the sword looked sharp, Belle…
   A. struck a piece of wood to prove it.
   B. promised to handle it carefully

9. Because Caleb had *trespassed*, the police…

    A.   told him that everything was fine and let him go.

    B.   gave him a ticket and told him never to return to the property.

10. Jocelynn *intended* her statement to be…

    A.   clever, but instead, it offended me.

    B.   the title of her book report on *Harry Potter*.

Exercise III – Crossword Puzzle

Use the clues and the words from this lesson to complete the crossword puzzle.

Across

5. Carter _____ that he didn't understand the math problem, so the teacher explained it again.

6. Even though it's silly, some people believe _____ about the number 13.

7. No army is _____, no matter how much it believes it is.

8. Because only a[n] _____ of the family wanted burgers, Dad drove to a seafood restaurant.

9. In spite of the sign, we were so tired that we decided to _____ on the farmer's land and take a shortcut home.

Down

1. What was that comment about my shoes _____ to mean?

2. Getting my triplets ready for the first day of school was rushed and _____.

3. The fire caused a[n] _____ amount of damage to the restaurant; it was closed for months.

4. Coffee is one of Brazil's biggest _____, along with iron.

6. The _____ where Lincoln delivered the Gettysburg Address has a plaque explaining what happened there.

Exercise IV – Critical Reading

Carefully read the passage and then choose the best answer for each of the questions that follow. The passage contains vocabulary words from the lesson.

The year is 1948. You're living in West Berlin. Your half of the city, controlled by the United States and its allies, is right in the middle of Soviet-controlled East Germany. The Soviet Union has just decided to block any trucks or trains to Berlin, which means no more supplies. To **trespass** on the ground of East Germany would
5　be an act of war. Since the end of World War II, you have had every **commodity** you needed—food, clothes, fuel, etc. Now, they are gone. Whatever stockpiles you had are quickly running out. Your friends and family are on the verge of starvation.

As food ran out, the United States engaged in **hectic** negotiations with the Soviet Union. The Soviets continued to deny road or rail traffic to Berlin, but agreed to allow
10　airplanes to fly there. With the clock ticking, the US had to come up with a plan to fly several thousand tons of food to West Berlin every single day. They **intended** to solve the crisis with an operation now known as the Berlin Airlift. It became the largest air supply mission in history. During the 15-month blockade, the US and its allies carried over two million tons of flour, coal, and other necessities to West Berlin.
15　The successful effort required almost 300,000 flights and hundreds of pilots.

One pilot, US Air Force Lieutenant Gail Halvorsen, was waiting for his plane to be unloaded in between supply runs. He noticed some of the poor local children near the runway fence. He gave them some gum, and they were thrilled. Flour and coal might have kept them alive during the airlift, but they were clearly missing out on some
20　of the simplest childhood joys. Halvorsen realized how **significant** a single piece of candy could be to the spirits of the children. He decided to take on a new duty.

During his many supply runs, Halvorsen attached candy to tiny parachutes. He dropped the candy from his plane over West Berlin. To the cheering children below, he quickly became a star. They called him the "Candy Bomber." After a few months,
25　Halvorsen's bosses noticed what was happening and the good effect it had on the morale of the people of West Berlin. The operation commander supported the new "mission," calling it Operation Little Vittles. Soon, dozens of pilots began making their own handkerchief parachutes. All these pilots dropped candy to the delighted children on the ground. Donations of candy and handkerchiefs poured in. After
30　six months, pilots had dropped more than 23 tons of sweet treats at different **sites** around West Berlin.

Halvorsen returned to America before Operation Little Vittles was over. The Air Force gave him a permanent job and paid for him to go to college. Even after retiring, Colonel Halvorsen did candy-drop missions in other war-torn places, such as Kosovo
35　and Iraq. His actions remind everyone that, sometimes, the smallest acts of kindness can be the most memorable.

Exercise IV – Critical Reading Questions

1. The author of this passage would probably agree with which one of the following statements?
    A. Dropping candy was more important than delivering food.
    B. Comfort and joy mean nothing when survival is a concern.
    C. The Air Force needed more supplies of candy than it was given.
    D. Colonel Halvorsen saw Operation Little Vittles through to the end.
    E. During busy times, small but important details can be forgotten.

2. Choose the statement that provides evidence to support your answer to the previous question.
    A. "They intended to solve the crisis with an operation now known as the Berlin Airlift." (lines 11-12)
    B. "Flour and coal might have kept them alive during the airlift, but they were clearly missing out on some of the simplest childhood joys." (lines 18-20)
    C. "During his many supply runs, Halvorsen attached candy to tiny parachutes. He dropped the candy from his plane over West Berlin." (lines 22-23)
    D. "Halvorsen returned to America before Operation Little Vittles was over." (line 32)
    E. "The Air Force gave him a permanent job and paid for him to go to college." (lines 32-33)

3. In line 6, *stockpiles* most nearly means
    A. shortages.
    B. businesses.
    C. firewood.
    D. supplies.
    E. weapons.

4. Choose the best title for this passage.
    A. Candy from the Sky: Halvorsen Drops Smiles
    B. What Was Behind the Berlin Airlift
    C. Saving West Berlin through Candy
    D. A History of West Berlin
    E. Operation Little Vittles: Feeding Berlin

5. What caused the Berlin Airlift?
    A. The children of West Berlin did not have enough food to be healthy.
    B. The Soviet Union blocked supplies to West Berlin.
    C. World War II left Germany without much food.
    D. Flying was the most efficient way to send supplies.
    E. Colonel Halvorsen needed to get more candy for the children of West Berlin.

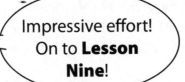

Lesson Nine

agitate
A-JIH-TAYT

v. to cause to become upset or excitedly troubled
Poking my dog's nose doesn't even *agitate* him.
syn: bother　　*ant: comfort; soothe*

archaeology
AR-KEE-**AHL**-UH-GEE

n. the study of prehistoric cultures by examining buildings, art, and tools
Jerome's book about *archaeology* contained drawings of what ancient cities probably looked like.

benefit
BEN-EH-FIT

v. to be helpful to or to receive help
A traffic light would *benefit* the town because there are many accidents at the intersection.
syn: assist; improve　　*ant: harm; injure*

conscience
KAHN-SHENS

n. a person's awareness of right and wrong
Nan's *conscience* bothered her, and she returned the doll she had stolen from the toy store.

controversial
KAHN-TROH-**VER**-SHUL

adj. causing disagreement
Grandpa loves to argue, so we try to avoid *controversial* topics around him.
ant: definite; undisputed

courteous
KUR-TEE-US

adj. polite and respectful
The *courteous* guests offered to help with the dishes after dinner.
syn: civil; considerate　　*ant: rude*

descendant
DEE-**SEN**-DENT

n. the relative of an earlier group of people
I heard that Charlie might be a *descendant* of George Washington.
syn: successor; offspring　　*ant: ancestor*

span

SPAN

v. to stretch between two points in time or space

There were so many clothes on the floor that the mess *spanned* the area from the bed to the door.

syn: connect; cross

temporary

TEM-PIH-RER-EE

adj. lasting for a short period of time

We used a tarp as a *temporary* roof after a fallen tree smashed a hole in the side of the house.

syn: limited   *ant: permanent*

woe

WOH

n. sorrow and misery

Life under the evil king was a time of *woe* for the people of Barkadia.

syn: suffering; distress   *ant: joy; delight*

Exercise I – Words in Context

Using the list of vocabulary words, supply the correct word to complete each sentence.

1. We planned a fundraiser that would _____ patients at the children's hospital.

2. Be _____ and shake the hand of any new person you meet.

3. Principal Dorfman canceled the assembly because the speaker wanted to discuss something _____.

4. Celia prefers warm weather; snowstorms and strong winds _____ her.

5. Aimee's mom studies _____; she knows a great deal about the history of Rome.

6. If you ever have any _____, come talk to me, and I will try to make you feel better.

7. Your feelings of guilt come from your _____, which is telling you that you did something wrong.

8. The flu spread and soon _____ across the entire country.

9. Our stay at the hotel is _____; we will be there for only a week or so.

10. The scientist explained how our pet dogs are _____ of wolves.

Exercise II – Finish the Sentence

First, choose the ending for each sentence that makes the best sense with the italicized vocabulary word used. Then, write your own ending for each sentence that shows you understand the meaning of the vocabulary word.

1. Because we couldn't watch the *controversial* movie…
    A. we were able to write a review of the film.
    B. we didn't know why it caused such a fuss.

2. The little boy didn't know how to be *courteous* because…
    A. his father never taught him manners.
    B. he had always been a quiet child.

3. Yolanda is looking for a *temporary* job that…
    A. she could do this summer before school starts.
    B. would help her learn new things over time.

4. Morgan experienced real *woe* when…
    A. he was separated from his family during the war.
    B. he wore his ghost costume on Halloween.

5. I want to learn about *archaeology* so that I can…
    A. teach about the planets and stars.
    B. learn how ancient people lived.

6. The *descendants* of the settlers of the original colony…
    A. were not related to the founders of that colony.
    B. heard the stories of the dangers their grandparents had faced.

7. Whenever Flo's *conscience* bothers her, she…
    A. thinks about whether her actions were right or wrong.
    B. makes sure she isn't late for a meeting.

8. Some *benefits* of moving to the country are…
    A. threats of wildlife and being far away from the city.
    B. lots of space to run and big, blue skies.

9. If you *agitate* a dog on purpose,…

    A. the dog will become afraid of strangers.

    B. don't be surprised if it bites you.

10. The long bridge was able to *span*…

    A. the travelers over to the other side.

    B. the full width of the river.

Exercise III – Crossword Puzzle

Use the clues and the words from this lesson to complete the crossword puzzle.

Across

1. Nothing _____ me more than having to repeat everything I say to my grandmother.

6. We had a[n] _____ power outage during the storm, but electricity was restored a few hours later.

7. Glenn had some very _____ and silly ideas about the benefits of playing video games.

8. If you don't do the regular work that's required, how can extra credit _____ you?

10. It's important to be _____ to people who have opinions that are different from yours; there will be many.

Down

2. I know that _____ will be my career because ancient cultures fascinate me.

3. "My _____ is clear; I did not cheat on the test!" insisted Alexa.

4. The best thing you can do is leave your _____ a better world than the one you were born in.

5. The retired baseball player's career _____ three decades.

9. In the story, the witch promised a year of _____ and sorrow on the prince's family.

Exercise IV – Improving Paragraphs

Carefully read the passage and then choose the best answer for each of the questions. The questions will ask you to make changes to improve the writing of the passage.

1   In September 1940, near the small town of Montignac, France, four teenage boys discovered a strange hole in the ground. Hoping it was the entrance to a secret tunnel, the boys excitedly climbed inside the dark cave with a small lantern. What they found was breathtaking. There were large paintings of bulls, horses, and bears on the cave's walls. Stick-figure people stood alongside the animal drawings. The darkness continued much farther into the huge cavern. <u>The boys couldn't explore them with their tiny lantern, though.</u> **{1}**

2   Soon, hundreds of people journeyed to Lascaux Cave. The famous archaeologist Henri Breuil concluded that the paintings **span** at least 17,000 years of human history. However, experts in archaeology and history argued over the meaning of the ancient cave paintings.

3   [1] Some believed the drawings were records of prehistoric wildlife because the animals shown in the paintings existed in France at one time. [2] The artists might have drawn the pictures for their **descendants** to learn about their ancestors. [3] Other experts thought the drawings represented stars and constellations because their patterns are similar to Orion's Belt, the Big Dipper, and the Taurus constellation. [4] Astronomers have contributed a lot of helpful information to other scientists. **{2}**

4   Before long, the large number of visitors **agitated** the delicate environment of the cave. <u>When people breathed all over in the cave, they released carbon dioxide into the air.</u> **{3}**The extra carbon dioxide caused the colors to fade. The visitors' body heat and light from flashlights also contributed to mold growth. After much debate, the French government closed Lascaux Cave to the public in order to preserve the paintings.

5   The French teenagers promised each other to keep the cave a secret, but their agreement was only **temporary**. The teens decided to bring their schoolteacher, Leon Laval, to the cavern. As soon as Laval saw the massive paintings, he knew the boys had made one of the greatest discoveries in **archaeology**.

6   Since 1963, only a few researchers have visited Lascaux Cave. Although tourists cannot see the original paintings, they can visit a nearby site named Lascaux II. This manmade cavern is an exact replica of the ancient location, complete with similar animal paintings. As they descend into Lascaux II, visitors can experience the same sense of speechless wonder those four teenagers did long ago. **{4}{5}**

Exercise IV – Improving Paragraphs Questions

1. Which choice shows the best way to correct the underlined sentence?
   A. Though the boys couldn't explore them with their tiny lantern.
   B. The boys couldn't explore the caves with their tiny lantern, though.
   C. The boys, with their tiny lanterns, couldn't explore them, though.
   D. The boys couldn't explore it with their tiny lantern, though.

2. One of the sentences in paragraph 3 does not contribute anything useful. Choose which sentence should be deleted.
   A. sentence 1
   B. sentence 2
   C. sentence 3
   D. sentence 4

3. Some of the words in the underlined sentence are unnecessary. Choose the phrase that should be deleted.

   "When people breathed all over in the cave, they released carbon dioxide into the air."

   A. in the cave
   B. all over
   C. they released
   D. carbon dioxide

4. Paragraph 5 is out of place but still belongs in the passage. Choose where the paragraph should be placed.
   A. before paragraph 1
   B. before paragraph 2
   C. before paragraph 3
   D. before paragraph 4

5. The writer wants to include more information about why the French banned tourists from Lascaux Cave. Choose the paragraph into which that information should be placed.
   A. paragraph 2
   B. paragraph 3
   C. paragraph 4
   D. paragraph 5

Review: Lessons 7-9

Exercise I – Related Words

Choose the word that best completes the sentence.

1. The *majority* of students hate the idea of wearing a uniform; only a _____ of them approve.
    A. commodity
    B. descendant
    C. minority
    D. nomad
    E. span

2. "In good *conscience*, I cannot let you go out in such a[n] _____ blizzard," said Ralph.
    A. invincible
    B. controversial
    C. temporary
    D. treacherous
    E. extravagant

3. Items found at the _____ have puzzled even those who are considered experts in *archaeology*.
    A. woe
    B. minority
    C. site
    D. commodity
    E. descendant

4. Danny says a lot of *controversial* things; remember when he _____ that "School is stupid"?
    A. agitated
    B. radiated
    C. trespassed
    D. intended
    E. remarked

5. _____ would consider portable items to be an important *commodity*.

    A. Nomads

    B. Sites

    C. Descendants

    D. Superstitions

    E. Consciences

6. You will _____ if you *finance* your own college tuition and don't take out a loan.

    A. amplify

    B. benefit

    C. emphasize

    D. intend

    E. remark

7. You might have some *temporary* nervousness during the _____ events at the gymnastics competition.

    A. courteous

    B. significant

    C. treacherous

    D. preliminary

    E. controversial

8. Mr. Reese made sure to _____ only the *significant* facts from the chapter.

    A. finance

    B. emphasize

    C. span

    D. benefit

    E. agitate

Exercise II – Synonyms and Antonyms

Match the word with its synonym.

1. _____ preliminary		**A.**	bother
2. _____ trespass		**B.**	lavish
3. _____ invincible		**C.**	stress
4. _____ benefit		**D.**	intrude
5. _____ extravagant		**E.**	indestructible
6. _____ agitate		**F.**	initial
7. _____ emphasize		**G.**	improve

Match the word with its antonym.

8. _____ inspire		**H.**	safe
9. _____ significant		**I.**	permanent
10. _____ treacherous		**J.**	calm
11. _____ hectic		**K.**	decrease
12. _____ controversial		**L.**	discourage
13. _____ temporary		**M.**	trivial
14. _____ amplify		**N.**	undisputed

Remarkable job! On to **Lesson Ten**!

Lesson Ten

confide
KAHN-**FIYD**

v. to reveal a secret to a trusted person

I *confide* all my secrets only to my closest friends.

syn: entrust

dejected
DIH-**JEK**-TED

adj. feeling sad and depressed

Jordan did not receive any valentines, which made her feel *dejected*.

syn: discouraged   *ant: cheerful; excited*

dishearten
DIS-**HAR**-TIN

v. to destroy hope or spirit

The gymnast did not let any of his mistakes in tumbling *dishearten* him.

syn: discourage; depress   *ant: encourage*

entrepreneur
AHN-TRIH-PREH-NOR

n. a person who owns or runs a business

Most *entrepreneurs* take out ads trying to sell their product.

syn: businessperson

frontier
FRUN-**TEER**

n. the land beyond the edge of a settled area; the limit of knowledge

The discovery of germs in the 1800s opened a new *frontier* of medicine.

fugitive
FYOO-JIH-TIV

n. a person who runs away to escape, often from the law

Mr. Bing went to jail for having helped hide his brother, a *fugitive* wanted for armed robbery.

syn: runaway; refugee

inquire
IN-**KWIYR**

v. to ask a question

Will you *inquire* about when band will begin playing?

syn: query   *ant: answer*

proceed

PROH-**SEED**

v. to continue forward

After a short break, we will *proceed* with the rest of the musical.

syn: progress; advance   *ant: stop*

swift

SWIFT

adj. moving or able to move very quickly

In one *swift* motion, the magician pulled the tablecloth out from under the dishes.

syn: rapid   *ant: slow*

vast

VAST

adj. great in area or number

The field the farmers use is *vast*, continuing for many miles.

syn: enormous; massive   *ant: little; small*

Exercise I – Words in Context

Using the list of vocabulary words, supply the correct word to complete each sentence.

1. I felt _____ when you forgot that today is my birthday.

2. The _____ motion of the squirrel darting across the lawn frightened my cat.

3. The police officer found a[n] _____ hiding in the library's basement.

4. I looked at the map my teacher handed out, but I had to _____ what the red lines meant.

5. During the sleepover, Debra _____ to her friends that she had a crush on Marco.

6. Seeing a new family in Jemma's old house _____ Monique deeply.

7. I prefer the _____, away from the village, because of its peace and quiet.

8. A good _____ knows the best way to make a company successful.

9. To reach your seats, you should _____ to the end of the row on your left.

10. There are _____ possibilities of things you can do with a chunk of clay.

Exercise II – Finish the Sentence

First, choose the ending for each sentence that makes the best sense with the italicized vocabulary word used. Then, write your own ending for each sentence that shows you understand the meaning of the vocabulary word.

1. Lionel felt *dejected* after his friend…
  A. moved to a new town.
  B. found a puppy.

2. Because history is such a *vast* subject,…
  A. I won't be able to tell you every last detail.
  B. let's talk about science instead.

3. Ben made a *swift* recovery once he…
  A. was admitted to the hospital for months.
  B. took a day off to rest his leg.

4. Marv knew he had become a successful *entrepreneur* when he…
  A. made one million dollars through his small business.
  B. won an award from the city for volunteering his time.

5. After a long night, the *fugitive* knew…
  A. that seeing the stars was simply wonderful.
  B. that he had to find somewhere to hide.

6. Bison roamed America's *frontier* before…
  A. settlers built towns and cities there.
  B. animal control caught them and took them back.

7. It's impossible to *proceed* with the hike if…
  A. we don't take a few pictures.
  B. our feet are covered with blisters.

8. The tourists stopped at the information booth to *inquire* about…
  A. the kids who were littering the park.
  B. the cost of tickets to the museum.

9. Brad said, "For me to *confide* in you, Nate, you…
   A. need to promise you won't tell anyone my secret."
   B. must prove to me that you want to help the homeless."

10. After listening for a couple minutes, Dad said, "I hate to *dishearten* you, Maureen, but…
   A. I'm not letting you go to the mall tonight."
   B. Mexico is on the southern border of the United States."

Exercise III – Crossword Puzzle

Use the clues and the words from this lesson to complete the crossword puzzle.

Across

2. Pioneers had to cross the _____ prairie by wagons in order to reach California.

6. Your task is to _____ about the price of park admission while I get prices for plane tickets.

8. The guide warned the tourists to _____ with caution up the stairs carved into the side of the cliff.

9. He was a great _____, and he also invented a tiny computer, smaller than a dime.

10. If you _____ in me, I won't tell anyone what you say.

Down

1. Kloszak became a[n] _____ and hid from the Nazis for three years during the war.

3. The president promised to take _____ action in response to the terrorist attack.

4. My dog looked _____ when I put away her favorite toy.

5. I had studied Spanish for days before the test, so my *C-* grade really _____ me.

7. Before settlers began moving across the country to the West, Ohio was America's western _____.

Exercise IV – Critical Reading

Carefully read the passage and then choose the best answer for each of the questions that follow. The passage contains vocabulary words from the lesson.

"The British are coming!" When most people hear this legendary phrase, they think of Paul Revere. In 1775, Revere galloped twenty miles through towns near Concord, Massachusetts, warning people that British soldiers were on their way. In doing so, he claimed his place as a hero in American history. But fewer people know
5   about the young girl who rode twice as far in a similar situation two years later. Sybil Ludington, a fiery and energetic sixteen-year-old, rode **vast** distances to warn her neighbors that British troops were about to attack the town of Danbury, Connecticut.

Sybil Ludington's father, Henry Ludington, was a veteran of the French and Indian War. Because of his experience, he was appointed head of the militia for all
10   of Duchess County, New York. When Henry heard that British troops were planning to attack Danbury, he asked Sybil to gather the militia. He worried that the British would destroy or steal the Continental Army's supplies and ammunition. Sybil **proceeded** to get on her horse and ride off in the pouring rain.

As the oldest of twelve children, Sybil was a responsible teenager. Riding through
15   the stinging rain was difficult for both Sybil and her horse. She also had to defend herself against an attacker. But even that couldn't **dishearten** her. She stopped only to tell members of the militia to meet at her father's house. She covered forty miles at a **swift** pace, riding from 9:00 p.m. to sunrise. When Sybil got home, over 400 men had already arrived, prepared to engage the British at Danbury. Unfortunately,
20   the town had already been attacked. The British had burned some buildings to the ground, but the militia was able to chase the remaining soldiers away. The militia then battled them at Ridgefield seventeen miles away.

When Sybil grew up, she married Edmond Ogden and had a son named for her father. They lived a quiet life on their family farm. At the time, it was considered
25   inappropriate for girls to have public recognition, so Sybil and her family **confided** in few about her own midnight ride. George Washington thanked her, but her ride was mostly forgotten until 1880, when her great-grandson wrote about her. Today, there are statues in her honor, and her hometown has been renamed Ludingtonville. There's even a race in her honor that covers part of her path on that rainy night in
30   1777.

Exercise IV – Critical Reading Questions

1. Why is Sybil Ludington famous?
    A. Her father defended Danbury from an attack by the British.
    B. Her great-grandson wrote a book about the Revolutionary War.
    C. She defended herself against a robber.
    D. She alerted troops to a coming attack.
    E. She helped Paul Revere on his midnight ride.

2. Sybil's ride took her forty miles around the countryside. What can you conclude about the militia from the distance Sybil had to cover?
    A. The members of the militia did not all come from one town.
    B. Many of the soldiers had been killed in battle, and she needed new ones.
    C. The militia didn't trust Sybil, a woman, to give them orders.
    D. The soldiers were not able to ride as long as Sybil did and couldn't follow her.
    E. The members of the militia were extremely loyal and dependable.

3. Choose the line from the passage that best supports your answer to the previous question.
    A. "When most people hear this legendary phrase, they think of Paul Revere." (lines 1-2)
    B. "Fewer people know about the young girl who rode twice as far in a similar situation two years later." (lines 4-5)
    C. "She covered forty miles at a swift pace, riding from 9:00 p.m. to sunrise." (lines 17-18)
    D. "Sybil proceeded to get on her horse and ride off in the pouring rain." (lines 12-13)
    E. "Because of his experience, he was appointed head of the militia for all of Duchess County, New York." (lines 9-10)

4. As it is used in line 19, *engage* mostly nearly means
    A. meet.
    B. fight.
    C. talk to.
    D. see.
    E. surrender to.

5. Choose the most appropriate title for the passage.
    A. Heroes Lost to History: Paul Revere's Helpers
    B. Why the British Must Be Stopped in Connecticut
    C. The Importance of the Colonial Militia
    D. Henry Ludington Saves Danbury
    E. The Other Revolutionary War Rider

You've got this! On to **Lesson Eleven**!

Lesson Eleven

contrast

KAHN-**TRAST**

v. to show the differences between things

The bright red tablecloth *contrasts* with the white curtains, carpet, and table.

syn: separate

equivalent

EE-**KWIV**-UH-LENT

adj. equal in quantity or function

The vitamin provides the *equivalent* amount of vitamin C as you get from eating an orange.

syn: alike; identical   *ant: unequal; different*

feat

FEET

n. a skillful or impressive action or achievement

Annalisa received a prize for her *feat* of running a five-minute mile.

syn: exploit; deed   *ant: failure*

herbivore

URB-IH-VOR

HURB-IH-VOR

n. an animal that eats only plants

Do not try to feed a sheep meat; sheep are *herbivores*.

misleading

MIS-**LEE**-DING

adj. causing confusion, sometimes intentionally

The movie about football had a *misleading* title: *Stolen Base.*

syn: tricky; false   *ant: honest; accurate*

obtain

UB-**TAYN**

v. to get; to take possession of

I collect snow globes and hope to *obtain* enough to fill my whole room.

syn: gain; acquire   *ant: lose*

rapid

RA-PID

adj. happening or moving at high speed

Stacy is great at speaking Spanish and can have *rapid* conversations with other speakers of the language.

syn: fast; quick   *ant: slow*

superb

SOO-**PURB**

adj. extremely good

The newspaper editor loved our school's production of the *Harry Potter* play, calling it *superb* in his article.

syn: superior; excellent　　*ant: inferior*

turnpike

TURN-PIYK

n. a road that usually requires a fee to be paid for using it

On the *turnpike*, you can drive from one end of Pennsylvania to the other.

syn: highway

vanquish

VAN-KWISH

v. to defeat in a battle or conflict

The large wrestler was easily able to *vanquish* his smaller opponent.

syn: conquer　　*ant: lose*

Exercise I – Words in Context

Using the list of vocabulary words, supply the correct word to complete each sentence.

1. After years of searching, Harold finally _____ the copy he was missing in his Superman comic book collection.

2. I thought goats are _____, but the one at the petting zoo tried to eat my ice cream cone.

3. Tonya's fingerprints all over the mirror were _____; it was actually Joey who had broken it.

4. When _____ with Jack's blond hair, Janelle's brown hair seems extra dark.

5. Juggling five tennis balls at once is a very impressive _____!

6. The workers closed off one lane of the _____ while they did construction.

7. The two homes appeared to be _____ in size, but one is much prettier.

8. When I do well on my homework, Mrs. Love gives me a sticker that says "_____."

9. Learning how to swim _____ Simon's lifelong fear of water.

10. When Carole pushed the wagon down the hill, there was a[n] _____ increase in speed.

Exercise II – Finish the Sentence

First, choose the ending for each sentence that makes the best sense with the italicized vocabulary word used. Then, write your own ending for each sentence that shows you understand the meaning of the vocabulary word.

1. The peach ripened at such a *rapid* pace that we…
   - A. thought it might go bad before we could eat it.
   - B. kept it out on the counter for a few more days.

2. The weather report can sometimes be *misleading*, so when the forecaster said it would be sunny,…
   - A. I packed an umbrella just in case.
   - B. we knew our picnic would be perfect.

3. The age of the three children was *equivalent* to…
   - A. seven, ten, and thirteen.
   - B. the age of their father.

4. Even though the service wasn't great, the meal was so *superb* that we…
   - A. complained to the manager.
   - B. left the waiter a tip anyway.

5. The show was terrific, but the dancer's most amazing *feat* was when she…
   - A. jumped and performed a split in midair.
   - B. twirled and showed off her beautiful dress.

6. Most *herbivores* have flat teeth that they use to…
   - A. bite into their prey.
   - B. chew grass and leaves.

7. *Turnpikes* can make a trip…
   - A. take longer than expected if there is a traffic jam.
   - B. into an adventure as you explore less-traveled roads.

8. I asked the doctor where she *obtained*…
   - A. her medical degree and certification.
   - B. her lunch break when working long shifts.

105

9. All it took to *vanquish* my favorite team was…

    A. a bad mistake that allowed the other team to score a goal.

    B. the decision to make a play that ended the game in a tie.

10. This great book report certainly *contrasts* with…

    A. another student's well-done project.

    B. my classmate's poorly written paper.

Exercise III – Crossword Puzzle

Use the clues and the words from this lesson to complete the crossword puzzle.

Across

1. Customers were willing to pay high prices for a taste of the chef's _____ chicken soup.

5. Your comment was not just a mistake; it was very _____.

8. To my dad, getting a *C* is the _____ of failing.

9. Some _____, like cows, have special stomachs designed to digest plants.

10. Even though we went only ten miles on the _____, the trip cost $7.75.

Down

2. Once Hamid received the right medicine, he made a[n] _____ recovery.

3. The rain fell all night, but today is bright and sunny—what a[n] _____!

4. The Romans expanded their empire and _____ all their enemies.

6. It took Lazlo more than three years to _____ a visa to come to the United States.

7. When the United States put a man on the moon, everyone agreed it was an amazing _____.

Exercise IV – Critical Reading

Carefully read the passage and then choose the best answer for each of the questions that follow. The passage contains vocabulary words from the lesson.

Children love to play social games such as "Tag," "Duck, Duck, Goose," and "Red Rover." Did you know that young animals like to play in groups, too? That's not all, either. Like kids, most young animals enjoy three different types of play: social play, object play, and locomotor play. Social play is group games or activities, like "Tag."

5 Object play involves toys or tools. Locomotor play is simply being in motion, whether that means walking, jumping, running, or even dancing.

Baby horses, or foals, love games so much that they play just days after they are born. They first exhibit locomotor play as they learn to gallop around and playfully nip at their mothers. Once they are a few weeks old, they begin to play socially,

10 alongside other young horses. They chase each other and race around each other in circles. They even include some object play, playing "catch" with each other using scrap boards, buckets, or twigs. At one month old, male and female horseplay begins to **contrast**. Colts, or males, enjoy play-fighting and climbing on top of their friends. Fillies, or females, prefer grooming each other and galloping from place to place.

15 Play-fighting is very common among animals, especially with animals known for their punches. Baby kangaroos, or joeys, like to battle with their mothers, but the mothers' participation in the game is **misleading**. The mother kangaroo never harms her baby; she keeps the game safe by pawing at the baby instead of punching with force. The mother and child have a signal they both use to remind each other that

20 the fighting is just a game.

Sometimes it is surprising to see which animals play. Who, for example, would think that crocodiles play? Crocodiles seem to participate in all three types of play. Observers have seen them sliding down riverbanks repeatedly for no obvious reason other than fun. Baby crocodiles chase each other and ride on each other's backs. They even play

25 with "toys," which means, of course, the unlucky animals that will be eaten later.

Some animals are best known for their object play. Cats, like crocodiles, are famous for tossing and battering their captured mice, birds, and insects. Horses are **herbivores**, so they don't play with dead prey, but they will spend hours chasing around a beach ball tossed into a corral. Dogs adore toys in any form, and baby

30 chimpanzees even carry around sticks that seem to be the **equivalent** of dolls.

Play might seem like simple fun, but really, it is necessary for survival. Play helps young animals grow and learn. Locomotor and object play sharpen animals' balance and exercise the muscles they need to flee from danger or capture prey. Animals that live in groups or herds have social structures. Playing with other animals teaches

35 them about limits, like how hard play-bites can be, how much food one animal can take from others, or how much to trust each other. Playing is really an education in which animals learn skills and prepare for their adult lives.

Exercise IV – Critical Reading Questions

1. As it is used on line 8, the word *exhibit* means
  - A. do battle with.
  - B. defend.
  - C. display.
  - D. artifact.
  - E. show off.

2. In this passage, a cat's killing a mouse is offered as an example of
  - A. social play.
  - B. herbivore behavior.
  - C. motherly behavior.
  - D. locomotor play.
  - E. object play.

3. The author would agree with which statement?
  - A. Animals would die without play.
  - B. Scientists do not understand animal play.
  - C. Play is completely different from one animal to the next.
  - D. Animals play only with their own kind.
  - E. There seems to be no purpose of animal play.

4. Choose the sentence that supports your answer to Question 3.
  - A. "Crocodiles seem to participate in all three types of play." (line 22)
  - B. "Locomotor play is simply being in motion, whether that means walking, jumping, running, or even dancing." (lines 5-6)
  - C. "Play helps young animals grow and learn." (lines 31-32)
  - D. "Play might seem like simple fun, but really, it is necessary for survival." (line 31)
  - E. "Animals that live in groups or herds have social structures." (lines 33-34)

5. This passage would most likely be included in a book about
  - A. raising horses.
  - B. American farms.
  - C. animal behavior.
  - D. choosing a pet.
  - E. wild animals.

Power up!
On to **Lesson Twelve**!

Vocabulary
Power Plus ❺
Vocabulary, Reading, and
Writing Exercises

Lesson Twelve

campaign
KAM-**PAYN**

n. a series of actions intended to accomplish a goal

We need to make posters and buttons to help Flora with her *campaign* for class president.

syn: operation; drive

collision
KUH-**LIH**-ZHUN

n. a crash between two or more things

The victims of the highway *collision* were taken away by an ambulance.

syn: wreck

communicate
KUM-**YOO**-NIH-KAYT

v. to give or spread information to others

While I am in Taiwan, I can *communicate* only through email.

syn: convey; correspond

consistent
KAHN-**SIS**-TENT

adj. reliable and steady

I've done the math problem three times and get the same *consistent* answer each time.

syn: constant; stable   *ant: random*

interfere
IN-TUR-FEER

v. to intrude in the activities or plans of others

The dog trainer prefers that the dog owners do not *interfere* with her methods.

syn: meddle; block

native
NAY-TIV

adj. born in or from a certain place

Native to Paris, Gwen tells many stories about growing up there.

syn: local   *ant: foreign*

poverty
PAH-VUR-TEE

n. the state of lacking necessary things, especially food or money

Nina had lived in *poverty* and sometimes didn't know when she would eat next.

syn: poorness   *ant: wealth*

resolution
REZ-UH-**LOO**-SHUN

n. the answer to a problem; a course of action

The two girls hugged after reaching a *resolution* to their disagreement.

syn: solution

scarce
SCAIRS

adj. not enough to meet demand

Water is a *scarce* resource in our solar system, which makes Earth quite special.

syn: limited; rare   *ant: plentiful*

simulate
SIM-YOO-LAYT

v. to copy or to create a copy of

The new video game *simulates* a real historic battlefield.

syn: imitate; reproduce

Exercise I – Words in Context

Using the list of vocabulary words, supply the correct word to complete each sentence.

1. My New Year's _____ is to make many new friends.

2. The goggles he wore for the experiment _____ being unable to see objects that are far away.

3. A game of tag caused a[n] _____ between two kids who were not looking where they were running.

4. Isabel is from Spain and finds it much easier to read in her _____ language, Spanish.

5. Every winter, our club travels to the city and hands out food to those living in _____.

6. The price of coffee at the local shop stays _____; it has been $2.00 for ten years now.

7. Did Kimmy _____ with you over the phone or by text message?

8. We have a[n] _____ amount of flour left—definitely not enough to bake brownies.

9. Coach Ashley asked Joyce's dad to leave because he was trying to _____ with the game.

10. What do you think of Alesha's _____ to help the homeless?

Exercise II – Finish the Sentence

First, choose the ending for each sentence that makes the best sense with the italicized vocabulary word used. Then, write your own ending for each sentence that shows you understand the meaning of the vocabulary word.

1. Because Greg is a *consistent* foul shooter, the coach…
    A. always has him shoot the free throws.
    B. told him to practice his free throw.

2. That type of parrot is so *scarce* that scientists believe…
    A. the birds will not have enough food to survive.
    B. that it no longer lives in the wild.

3. The villagers are *native* to the mountains, so they…
    A. are used to the harsh conditions there.
    B. do not know much about walking there.

4. Most *collisions* on roads can be avoided if…
    A. drivers pay attention to other cars.
    B. people do not slow down.

5. The restaurant on the corner started a *campaign* to…
    A. get people to eat farm-fresh food.
    B. shorten its weekend hours.

6. The *poverty* of the people living there…
    A. attracted tourists to the area.
    B. was so bad that some children had no shoes.

7. This argument seems to have no *resolution*, so…
    A. I will leave rather than continue fighting.
    B. we both know that I am right.

8. Salvatore calmly said, "Please don't *interfere* with…
    A. your video game; you played it enough today."
    B. my weightlifting; I need to concentrate."

9. The police *simulated* a crime scene because…

    A. the original location had been destroyed in a fire.

    B. it didn't matter if the new scene was like the original or not.

10. It is important to *communicate*…

    A. your feelings before a final decision is made.

    B. a nice drawing to submit to the contest.

Exercise III – Crossword Puzzle

Use the clues and the words from this lesson to complete the crossword puzzle.

Across

3. The fish I own is _____ to the Amazon River, so I am lucky it survives in my aquarium.

5. The long _____ to stop people from smoking has been fairly successful.

6. Sometimes, my chores _____ with my homework, so I have to decide which is more important.

8. Kendy _____ to her dog only in German because the dog does not understand English commands.

9. Scientists fear a[n] _____ between Earth and a large comet or asteroid.

10. Our baseball team has had a[n] _____ winning record for the past five years.

Down

1. Jobs became _____ after the factory closed, so our family moved to a different state.

2. There was no _____ in the town because most people had well-paying jobs.

4. Dad calmly explained, "Since there is no good _____ to the fighting over what to watch on TV, you both need to go to bed immediately!"

7. To train astronauts, NASA _____ the conditions of zero-gravity space flight.

115

Exercise IV – Improving Paragraphs

Carefully read the passage and then choose the best answer for each of the questions. The questions will ask you to make changes to improve the writing of the passage.

1   For the most part, humans work during the day and sleep at night. Some animals, however, **consistently** sleep during the daytime. They are referred to as "nocturnal." Many of them sleep underground or inside a cave so the sun does not bother them. These creatures have special vision, hearing, and other senses that help them thrive at night.

2   [1] One of their special traits is night vision, which helps them see in the dark. [2] This way, they can find food and see predators while avoiding **collisions**. [3] There are many differences between the eyes of nocturnal animals and those of humans. [4] As you might imagine, their eyes are much larger. [5] An owl's eyes are shaped like tubes rather than spheres. [6] The tube shape lets more light into the eye, but it prevents owls from moving their eyes side-to-side. [7] Luckily, owls can turn their heads 270 degrees. **{1}**

3   Some nocturnal animals have better ears than eyes. Bats have echolocation, which is a way to see through hearing, much like a submarine's sonar allows the crew to see objects around the ship. Bats use it to find food, to stay away from predators, and to **communicate** with each other. **{2}** <u>While flying, bats make a high-pitched noise, and the noise the bats make bounces off objects nearby.</u> This sound usually comes out of a bat's mouth, but can sometimes come through its nose. A bat's echolocation pitches are so high that humans cannot hear them.

4   [1] Rabbits, like bats, have great hearing. [2] Though raccoons do not have thumbs, they can use their fingers to lift and handle food and other objects. [3] Rabbits' long, straight ears help them travel in the dark when light is **scarce**. [4] Good hearing is especially important for rabbits because of their poor vision. [5] Rabbits have difficulty understanding how far away an object is just from looking at it. [6] They also struggle with seeing things that are very close to them. [7] Their ears allow them to hear noises from far away, especially high-pitched noises, like those from a bat or a rodent. [8] A rabbit's ears move back and forth when upright because they are trying to locate the sound of any possible danger. **{3}**

5   Raccoons adapt **{4}** <u>to its nighttime</u> surroundings in an interesting way: They have extremely sensitive and skillful fingers on each paw. In particular, raccoons will use their hands to grab crayfish and other prey under rocks in streams and brooks at night. The taste and smell of the water helps raccoons absorb information about the environment around them.

6   Finally, some nocturnal animals may lack great eyes, ears, or fingers. Instead, they have special forms of self-defense to keep them safe at night. An opossum will foam at its mouth and play dead in order to look unappetizing to predators. Many pet dogs in porcupine country have learned the hard way to keep their noses far away from the sharp-quilled beasts. Even more have learned what happens if they **interfere** with a skunk on its nightly rounds. {5}

Exercise IV – Improving Paragraphs Questions

1. The writer wants to add the following sentence to paragraph 2:

    "One animal even has eyes that are half the size of its whole head."

    Choose where the sentence should be inserted.
    A. before sentence 1
    B. before sentence 2
    C. after sentence 4
    D. after sentence 7

2. This sentence from paragraph 3 contains unnecessary words. Choose the best revision of the underlined portion of the sentence.

    "While flying, bats make a <u>high-pitched noise, and the noise the bats make</u> bounces off of objects nearby."

    A. high-pitched noise
    B. high-pitched noise, and they
    C. high-pitched noise, the noise
    D. high-pitched noise that

3. Which sentence from paragraph 4 should be moved to paragraph 5?
    A. sentence 2
    B. sentence 4
    C. sentence 6
    D. sentence 8

4. Choose the best correction for the underlined portion of the sentence. *Be sure to read the whole sentence.*

    A. to they're nighttime

    B. to a nighttime

    C. too it's nighttime

    D. to their nighttime

5. Choose the sentence that would be the best way to conclude the entire passage.

    A. "No one knows for sure how much sleep these animals require."

    B. "These animals might not have the best senses, but they, too, have found ways to survive in their night world."

    C. "Dogs, cats, and horses are all animals that sleep at night."

    D. "Like rabbits, some dogs are small, but have good senses to make up for their small size."

Vocabulary Power Plus

Vocabulary, Reading, and Writing Exercises

Review: Lessons 10-12

Exercise I – Related Words

Choose the word that best completes the sentence.

1. A wealthy _____ donated a great deal of his earnings to people living in *poverty*.
    A. fugitive
    B. resolution
    C. feat
    D. entrepreneur
    E. herbivore

2. The *dejected* look on his best friend's face _____ Will.
    A. vanquished
    B. proceeded
    C. inquired
    D. disheartened
    E. contrasted

3. Sheila's powerful _____ helped her *vanquish* the other candidate in the election.
    A. campaign
    B. feat
    C. turnpike
    D. collision
    E. resolution

4. _____ about the best way to *communicate* with Josie while she's in Japan.
    A. Obtain
    B. Inquire
    C. Simulate
    D. Confide
    E. Proceed

5. We crossed a _____ desert before we reached the region's *frontier*.

    A. scarce

    B. misleading

    C. superb

    D. rapid

    E. vast

6. The _____ had to make another *rapid* escape once the police heard of his whereabouts.

    A. entrepreneur

    B. collision

    C. fugitive

    D. poverty

    E. campaign

7. To *simulate* a war zone, the video maker hired an ex-soldier to design a battlefield that would be the _____ of a real conflict.

    A. equivalent

    B. feat

    C. resolution

    D. turnpike

    E. poverty

8. Did you hear about the horrible *collision* involving five cars on the _____ today?

    A. resolution

    B. frontier

    C. campaign

    D. fugitive

    E. turnpike

Exercise II – Synonyms and Antonyms

Match the word with its synonym.

1. _____ proceed

A. excellent

2. _____ swift

B. wreck

3. _____ vanquish

C. progress

4. _____ interfere

D. accomplishment

5. _____ superb

E. conquer

6. _____ collision

F. rapid

7. _____ feat

G. meddle

Match the word with its antonym.

8. _____ misleading

H. encourage

9. _____ dejected

I. random

10. _____ obtain

J. plentiful

11. _____ consistent

K. excited

12. _____ dishearten

L. foreign

13. _____ scarce

M. honest

14. _____ native

N. lose

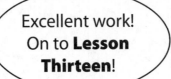

Excellent work! On to **Lesson Thirteen**!

Lesson Thirteen

boast
BOHST

v. to speak with excessive pride
When Sid's family bought a big boat, he *boasted* about it for days.
syn: brag

efficient
EH-**FISH**-ENT

adj. functioning well with little waste
An *efficient* captain takes the safest and shortest course to the destination.
syn: effective   *ant: wasteful*

feud
FYOOD

n. a long, bitter fight between groups, especially families or clans
For years, the two families kept up the *feud* and never settled their differences.
syn: quarrel   *ant: peace*

fury
FYUR-EE

n. violent and uncontrollable anger
Mom could not contain her *fury* when we knocked over her favorite lamp.
syn: anger; rage   *ant: calmness*

gradual
GRAD-JOO-ULL

adj. occurring in small steps
Walking up the hill was a slow, *gradual* process, but tumbling back down took only seconds.
syn: steady   *ant: rapid*

justification
JUS-TIH-FIH-**KAY**-SHUN

n. the reason for an action or a decision
"I was trying to find your blue sweater" was Vicky's *justification* for looking through my closet.
syn: explanation

perish
PER-ISH

v. to die or cease to be
At the end of the comic book, the evil alien *perished* at the hands of Queen Zirconia.
ant: survive; live

123

preserve
PREH-**ZURV**

v. to keep something in unchanged condition

The government *preserved* the old house on the corner as a national landmark.

syn: protect; maintain   *ant: ruin*

qualify
KWAHL-IH-FIY

v. to have the needed skills or abilities for something

Taking this class will *qualify* you all to perform first aid on injured people.

syn: certify

stationary
STAY-SHUN-ER-EE

adj. not moving; remaining in one place

My uncle kept the car *stationary* until the emergency vehicle passed us.

syn: immobile; fixed   *ant: wandering; loose*

Exercise I – Words in Context

Using the list of vocabulary words, supply the correct word to complete each sentence.

1. Trevor, a[n] _____ sculptor, does not waste any of his materials.

2. What was it exactly that caused the dinosaurs to _____?

3. Do you have any _____ for stealing my idea for the science fair?

4. Though you are lucky to have taken a trip to Scotland, you should not _____ about it.

5. The _____ between Sherrie and her neighbors began when they broke her front window.

6. The old bicycle remained _____ at the side of the house until I finally decided to ride it.

7. Though he was related to King George, the young prince did not have enough experience to _____ as a ruler.

8. The history museum keeps its items in display cases in order to _____ those objects.

9. Jordan reacted to the insult by grinding his teeth, a clear sign of his _____.

10. Once you become a teenager, you grow taller at a[n] _____ rate.

Exercise II – Finish the Sentence

First, choose the ending for each sentence that makes the best sense with the italicized vocabulary word used. Then, write your own ending for each sentence that shows you understand the meaning of the vocabulary word.

1. The view outside my window is *stationary*, and…
   A. even the leaves on trees aren't moving.
   B. it looks different with every glance.

2. For more *efficient* yard cleanup, Jessica…
   A. bought a leaf-blower that could do the job in minutes.
   B. paid some people to bring their rakes to her house to help.

3. The *gradual* increase in temperature…
   A. was the first thing the guests noticed after they arrived.
   B. went unnoticed until it was extremely hot in the room.

4. A *feud* between the two billionaires…
   A. allowed them to work together on new technology.
   B. began when one stole an idea from the other.

5. Our dog showed its *fury* by…
   A. growling when we tried to pet her.
   B. jumping and wagging her tail.

6. There cannot be any *justification* for…
   A. quitting in the middle of a game.
   B. throwing a fit if you lose a game.

7. Josh's talent is really something to *boast* about because he…
   A. is an excellent guitar player.
   B. can play tennis fairly well.

8. Only three people could *qualify* for…
   A. the high-level position at the company.
   B. fitting in the back seats of the car.

9. Many ancient civilizations *perished* because…

    A. they were able to build strong, high walls.

    B. floods or disease wiped out the population.

10. William swore that he would always *preserve* the memories of his child's birth by…

    A. thinking about the pictures he took on that day.

    B. creating a photo album with the pictures.

Exercise III – Crossword Puzzle

Use the clues and the words from this lesson to complete the crossword puzzle.

Across

4. My boss explained that if I become more _____ at my job, she will give me a raise.

7. What _____ is there for breaking your promise?

8. The hikers moved slowly, making _____ progress on the narrow trail.

9. After a few days, the _____ between us just seemed silly, and Davita and I made up.

10. It takes years of study and training to _____ as a heart surgeon.

Down

1. What is the best way to _____ pears so that they don't rot?

2. Right before the pirate _____ from his injuries, he mumbled something about a buried treasure.

3. The pilot fought to keep the helicopter perfectly _____ as he hovered over the struggling survivors in the rough sea below.

5. Alexa's sadness about her missing dog turned to _____ when she found out that someone had taken him.

6. Ira _____ about how great his essay was until he had to read it out loud in front of the class.

Exercise IV – Critical Reading

Carefully read the passage and then choose the best answer for each of the questions that follow. The passage contains vocabulary words from the lesson.

Egypt **boasts** the world's most famous mummies. However, Egyptian mummies, carefully wrapped in cloth and buried deep within large tombs, are not the only kind. Northern Europeans used to sink the dead in bogs, which are swampy mud pits. Several bodies have been found in bogs in and around the United Kingdom and

5 Germany. The bogs had mummified the people after they **perished**. Scientists say that some of the bodies have been there since 2000 BCE, making them more than 4,000 years old.

The first bog bodies were discovered in the 1600s. Bogs contain a mossy soil called peat, which also makes good fuel for burning. When people removed peat from

10 bogs to use as an **efficient** heat source, they uncovered bodies. They thought the dead had been recently murdered because the bodies looked well **preserved**, so they simply reburied them. In the 1800s, Fredrick VII, Prince of Denmark, suspected that the bodies might be older than originally thought, so he sent one to a museum to be studied. Scientists realized that the mummified people had not died recently.

15 The bog people don't look old because they were treated better than Egyptian mummies were. The cool mud protected the bodies from air, preventing normal decay. In addition, peat bog water is acidic, which has the effect of pickling the bodies and tanning the skin like leather. Some ancient bog bodies still have skin, hair, and organs. Because of this, it is often easy to tell how they died. By looking at

20 the marks on the mummies' bodies, scientists have found that most bog people were killed as punishment for crimes or in religious sacrifices.

Bog bodies were usually buried with clothes on. Sometimes they were even buried with personal items. Much of the clothing survived along with the mummies. The clothes, whether they are fancy or plain, provide evidence about the people who died,

25 how they died, and the lives they lived. Peat bogs often preserve hair, too, turning it red due to the acidic conditions. Even some hairstyles remain, especially on female bodies. For example, the Elling Woman, found in Denmark, still had her hair in a fancy braid. Another mummy, the Clonycavan Man from Ireland, had his hair styled with some ancient "gel" from France or Italy.

30 From small, well-preserved details, historians and scientists can learn much about the past from the bog people. No matter what the **justification** was for their deaths, the bog people have provided a gift of valuable information about ancient societies.

Exercise II – Finish the Sentence

First, choose the ending for each sentence that makes the best sense with the italicized vocabulary word used. Then, write your own ending for each sentence that shows you understand the meaning of the vocabulary word.

1. When you behave in a *juvenile* way,…

    A. your parents might tell you to act your age.

    B. your friends think you are being a snob.

2. Carlotta's friendly personality is completely *inseparable* from her…

    A. desire to be left alone.

    B. love for meeting new people.

3. It's not enough to simply be *prosperous* in your work because…

    A. you need to be able to afford what you need, too.

    B. family and friends really make life fulfilling.

4. The *prevailing* mood before the hurricane was…

    A. one of fear and worry as the whole town waited.

    B. indifference; Trent was not concerned.

5. My *anxiety* left as soon as…

    A. Denise reminded me that our project was due tomorrow.

    B. I realized I knew all the answers to the test.

6. Whatever *salary* Mr. Jeptha offered,…

    A. if the job was unpaid, I would work elsewhere.

    B. I would accept the position because it is my dream job.

7. Nina acted as a *representative* for her boss at the meeting because…

    A. her boss had an emergency and was unable to make it.

    B. Nina was too shy to talk to the strangers she would see.

8. Whenever Barb gets the chance, she *monitors* how…

    A. beautiful the painting looks.

    B. well her son is doing in math class.

9. From the teacher's look, the class could *infer* that…

    A. they were in trouble for misbehaving.

    B. she was wearing a new shade of lipstick.

10. I just cannot *abide* people who…

    A. read quietly at coffee shops.

    B. throw trash out of their car windows.

Exercise III – Crossword Puzzle

Use the clues and the words from this lesson to complete the crossword puzzle.

Across

4. Stop your _____ behavior and act your age!

6. The parents _____ the sleeping baby through a small security camera on her dresser.

7. Two _____ from Congress spoke to the class about the way the government worked.

9. The _____ business created jobs for thousands of people.

10. The sailboat battled a[n] _____ west wind and traveled slowly.

Down

1. If you want to swim at the public pool, you'll have to _____ by the rules, or you'll get thrown out.

2. The owner of the business pays everyone a good _____.

3. From the way you have been avoiding me, I can _____ that you don't want me around.

5. Some adult birds are _____ when they raise their young.

8. I have a lot of _____ when I have to read out loud in front of the class.

Exercise IV – Critical Reading

Carefully read the passage and then choose the best answer for each of the questions that follow. The passage contains vocabulary words from the lesson.

When Violet Jessop started working as a stewardess on a ship in 1908, she never thought of the risks. Within ten years, however, she had survived three major incidents at sea. But she did not allow the **anxiety** from the incidents to stop her from working.

5 Jessop was twenty-one when her mother became ill, so she had to find a job to help support the family. As a stewardess, Jessop was a servant for affluent guests who could afford the high price of sailing on large ships. Some of her duties involved cleaning, **monitoring** the deck, and delivering food. She made a **salary** of fifteen dollars a month, plus tips, food, and housing. Today, that would amount to only four

10 thousand dollars a year!

Stewarding was not a fun job, but Jessop didn't think it would be dangerous when she boarded the RMS *Olympic* in 1911, as long as she could **abide** the motion of the boat and not get seasick. The *Olympic* was a luxury cruising ship—the largest of its time. On September 20, 1911, the *Olympic* crashed into the HMS *Hawke*, a British

15 warship. Fortunately, they were not far from shore. The *Olympic* limped back to port for repairs. Though shaken, all the passengers and crewmembers survived.

Jessop's worst experience on a ship is also one of the biggest disasters in nautical history. In 1912, she joined the crew of the RMS *Titanic*, the doomed, massive luxury liner that is now famous for striking an iceberg on its maiden voyage. In the two

20 hours between the crash and the ship's sinking, Jessop performed her duties as a stewardess with grace. She helped passengers who could not speak English, showing them what to do. When Jessop finally boarded a lifeboat herself, she was handed a baby to look after. The child's mother found him the next day after the rescue. He and Jessop were two of the 706 survivors of the *Titanic*. More than 1,500 others had

25 disappeared beneath the icy, black waves, never to be seen again. A minor character in the 1997 film *Titanic* is meant to be **representative** of Jessop.

World War I was underway when Jessop boarded yet another huge ocean liner. She served on the HMHS *Britannic*. It had been outfitted as a floating hospital for the war effort. One morning in 1916, an explosion rocked the ship, sending it—

30 and thirty people—to the bottom of the Aegean Sea. No one knows exactly what caused the explosion, but many people point to an underwater mine as a possibility. This time, Jessop received severe head injuries and barely survived. In spite of her questionable luck, she continued to work at sea and enjoyed a **prosperous** career as a stewardess and nurse. Jessop retired in 1950 after having spent forty-two years at sea.

35 She died in 1971, but is still remembered as "Miss Unsinkable."

Exercise IV – Critical Reading Questions

1. According to information in the passage, what did the ships on which Violet Jessop served have in common?
   A. The ships all sank, and many people died.
   B. All were large, luxury ships.
   C. The ships were all military vessels.
   D. They were hospital ships.
   E. Each ship was bigger than the previous one.

2. As it is used in line 6, *affluent* most nearly means
   A. famous.
   B. traveling.
   C. numerous.
   D. wealthy.
   E. older.

3. Choose the most appropriate title for the passage.
   A. The History of the *Titanic*
   B. Surviving a Shipwreck
   C. The Unsinkable Violet Jessop
   D. An Important Woman on Three Ships
   E. Three Ships, Three Disasters

4. Based on the information in the passage, Jessop's experiences can be described as
   A. an argument against working aboard ships.
   B. inspiring to the families of those lost at sea.
   C. making the point that all experiences help a person grow.
   D. a result of either her good luck or her bad luck.
   E. her reason for working at sea.

5. Choose the line from the passage that best supports your answer to the previous question.
   A. "Some of her duties involved cleaning, monitoring the deck, and delivering food." (lines 7-8)
   B. "The *Olympic* limped back to port for repairs." (lines 15-16)
   C. "When Jessop finally boarded a lifeboat herself, she was handed a baby to look after." (lines 22-23)
   D. "This time, Jessop received severe head injuries and barely survived." (line 32)
   E. "In spite of her questionable luck, she continued to work at sea and enjoyed a prosperous career as a stewardess and nurse." (lines 32-34)

Awesome!!! On to **Lesson Fifteen**!

Lesson Fifteen

abbreviate
AH-**BREE**-VEE-AYT

v. to shorten
Almost everybody *abbreviates* "District of Columbia" to "D. C."
syn: condense; reduce   *ant: extend; lengthen*

blockade
BLAH-**KAYD**

n. something that halts or prevents progress or movement
The king ordered a *blockade* set up in the river to stop the Viking raiders.
syn: barricade; obstacle

compromise
KOM-PRUH-MIYZ

v. to reach an agreement by each side's giving up something it wanted
The twins decided to *compromise* and have their birthday party at a
place both of them liked, rather than argue over where it would be.
syn: negotiate   *ant: dispute; quarrel*

essential
EE-**SEN**-CHUL

adj. very important and necessary
If you have a cold, carrying tissues with you is *essential*.
syn: crucial; key   *ant: unimportant*

famine
FAM-IN

n. a widespread shortage of food
Crop failures throughout the country caused a two-year *famine* in which
many people starved.
                    ant: abundance; feast

hardship
HARD-SHIP

n. something that causes suffering or difficulty
Milo had survived many *hardships*, such as losing his parents at a young
age and fighting in two wars.
syn: burden   *ant: advantage*

hideous
HIH-DEE-US

adj. ugly and offensive to the senses or mind
"You look *hideous* in that monster mask!" laughed Arin.
syn: horrible; repulsive   *ant: delightful; pleasing*

phenomenon
FIH-**NAHM**-IH-NAHN

n. a strange or unexplained event or thing; something that occurs

Texting was once a rare *phenomenon*, but now, everyone does it.

syn: occurrence

reside
REH-**ZIYD**

v. to live in

The Turner family has *resided* in Mirksdale for ten years.

syn: inhabit; occupy

urgent
UR-JENT

adj. demanding immediate attention

A person who has a medical emergency should be brought to the *urgent* care unit.

syn: critical   *ant: unimportant*

Exercise I – Words in Context

Using the list of vocabulary words, supply the correct word to complete each sentence.

1. The loss of the family dog was a great _____ to the Morgansons.

2. A rainbow is a beautiful, natural _____ that can appear right after a rainstorm.

3. Stan thought he looked _____ in his glasses, but I thought they looked cool on him.

4. The _____ stopped the pirates from sneaking into the kingdom.

5. I knew we would be walking a great deal, so I packed only the _____ items.

6. Mom wanted to see a movie, and Dad wanted to go hiking; to _____, they watched a movie about hiking.

7. Having always had enough food, I could not imagine the horror of _____.

8. I had to _____ my speech when I realized that I was running out of time.

9. Call me back as soon as you can; I have something _____ to discuss with you.

10. For six weeks this summer, I will _____ in a cabin with ten other girls at sleepaway camp.

Exercise II – Finish the Sentence

First, choose the ending for each sentence that makes the best sense with the italicized vocabulary word used. Then, write your own ending for each sentence that shows you understand the meaning of the vocabulary word.

1. The mayor's office received an *urgent* request to…
   A. set up emergency shelters for people affected by the tornado.
   B. schedule a meeting with city council next month.

2. The museum had a display of *hideous* mummies that…
   A. frightened a group of young children.
   B. were largely forgotten by the tourists.

3. I know it's *essential* to…
   A. bring a book in case I get bored in the waiting room.
   B. arrive at the airport early so I don't miss my flight.

4. *Famine* hit the farming community hard, especially…
   A. after insects ate most of the crops.
   B. when the mayor was arrested for stealing.

5. The police set up *blockades* on the highways to…
   A. show the community that they were on duty.
   B. prevent the escaped criminal from leaving the area.

6. The hockey tournament became a *hardship* when…
   A. the travel expenses were more than we could afford.
   B. our team lost the final game against last year's champions.

7. The amazing runner who broke every world record was a *phenomenon* who…
   A. will be seen only once in a person's lifetime.
   B. will soon be replaced by the next great athlete.

8. How can you possibly *abbreviate*…
   A. a three-letter name?
   B. this twenty-page book report?

9. Ken will *reside* in…

    A. a group of six others when he hikes the trail.

    B. the same town in which he plans to attend college.

10. Jill needs to *compromise* with her sister because…

    A. they cannot agree on what movie to watch.

    B. Jill hurt her when they were fighting.

Exercise III – Crossword Puzzle

Use the clues and the words from this lesson to complete the crossword puzzle.

Across

1. The wealthy actor thought that having only five cars was some kind of awful _____.

5. Being able to swim more than a mile is a[n] _____ part of being a lifeguard.

6. "Mr." and "Mrs." are used to _____ the words "mister" and "missus."

7. This is _____; please stop what you're doing and come with me, quickly.

9. Knowing how to _____ is an important social skill.

10. Patrick created a[n] _____ out of cardboard boxes to keep his puppy out of the living room.

Down

2. The complexity of nature is apparent in the _____ of a caterpillar's becoming a butterfly.

3. The rare frog was _____, but oddly cute, too.

4. After the horrible, five-year-long drought, _____ set in, leading to many deaths.

8. No animal besides the penguin _____ year-round in Antarctica.

Exercise IV – Improving Paragraphs

Carefully read the passage and then choose the best answer for each of the questions. The questions will ask you to make changes to improve the writing of the passage.

1   From the deck of the CSS *Owl*, commanding officer John Newland Maffitt eyed the port of Galveston, Texas. Sixteen Union ships guarded the harbor. They prevented Confederate Navy ships like the *Owl* from bringing **essential** supplies to the South. But Maffitt was determined. He would run the **blockade**. He ordered his men to raise the sails and shovel coal to power the steam engine. {1} <u>As the *Owl* was steamed by the captain through the shallow waters near Galveston</u>, it became stuck on a sandbar. Union shells exploded around it. Maffitt kept a clear head, though. With the help of a Confederate gunboat, he was able to reach Galveston before any crewmembers were lost. The Union ships' cannons had damaged the *Owl*, but it managed to sneak past the North's ships once again.

2   [1] Maffitt's risks were not the actions of a fool. [2] **{2}** <u>Before joining the Confederates, he had served in the United States Navy in his uniform for about thirty years, having enlisted when he was only thirteen years old.</u> [3] During his service, Maffitt surveyed the coast and mapped ocean depths. [4] In 1857, Maffitt caught slave ships in the West Indies. [5] He became the first American officer to capture a ship filled with enslaved people. [6] Maffitt helped them return to Africa, their home continent, so they were saved from the horrible **hardships** of slavery. [7] Disease was also a major problem on slave ships. [8] When the Civil War began in 1861, Maffitt was forced to choose between his loyalty to North Carolina, where his children and family **resided**, or to the North. [9] A friend told him that the US government planned to arrest him because it believed he supported the South. {3}

3   Maffitt worked temporarily as a naval aide to General Robert E. Lee before being ordered to captain the steamer *Cecile*. His **urgent** mission was to deliver weapons and supplies to the South. For the rest of the war, Maffitt ran blockades and raided Union ships, capturing vessels and stealing their cargo for the Confederates. He gained a reputation as both a daring pirate and a gentleman who treated his enemies with respect.

4   As the South lost coastal cities to the Union, Maffitt was unwilling to **compromise** with the Northern victors. Instead, he ran a Union blockade one last time, taking heavy losses, and sailed to Britain.

5   There, he turned the *Owl* over to Confederate agents. He then took command of a British merchant ship for a few years before returning to North Carolina in 1868. {4} {5}

144

Exercise IV – Improving Paragraphs Questions

1. Choose the best way to rewrite the underlined portion of the sentence to make it more exciting.
   A. As the captain steamed the *Owl* through the shallow waters near Galveston
   B. As the *Owl* and the captain steamed through Galveston's shallow waters
   C. As the captain ordered the *Owl* to be steamed near Galveston through the shallow waters
   D. As the *Owl*, near Galveston and its shallow waters, steamed by the captain

2. Sentence 2 contains unnecessary language. Choose the phrase that should be deleted from the sentence because it does not add important information.

   "Before joining the Confederates, he had served in the United States Navy in his uniform for about thirty years, having enlisted when he was only thirteen years old."

   A. United States Navy
   B. in his uniform
   C. for about thirty years
   D. only thirteen years old

3. One sentence in paragraph 2 does not contribute any important details to the main idea. Choose the sentence that should be deleted.
   A. sentence 2
   B. sentence 4
   C. sentence 5
   D. sentence 7

4. The writer would like to include the following sentence in the passage:

   "Feeling betrayed, Maffitt resigned from the US Navy and joined the Confederate Navy."

   Choose the paragraph in which the sentence should be inserted.
   A. paragraph 1
   B. paragraph 2
   C. paragraph 4
   D. paragraph 5

5. Two of the paragraphs in the passage share a topic. They should be combined. Choose the two paragraphs that should be combined into one paragraph.

    A. paragraphs 1 and 4

    B. paragraphs 2 and 3

    C. paragraphs 4 and 5

    D. paragraphs 2 and 5

Exercise I – Related Words

Choose the word that best completes the sentence.

1. Thousands of people _____ during the *famine* that struck the city.
   A. compromised
   B. perished
   C. preserved
   D. boasted
   E. inferred

2. "I hope we can *preserve* at least some joy during this difficult _____," said Martin.
   A. phenomenon
   B. blockade
   C. fury
   D. hardship
   E. justification

3. Horatio is very _____; he has a yearly *salary* similar to that of movie stars.
   A. prosperous
   B. urgent
   C. stationary
   D. prevailing
   E. efficient

4. Both Giovani and Drew had to *compromise* in order to settle their _____.
   A. salary
   B. feud
   C. representative
   D. blockade
   E. anxiety

5. All *representatives* of the city who serve on the city council must actually _____ within city limits.

    A. perish

    B. infer

    C. reside

    D. compromise

    E. boast

6. Camp counselors must *abide* by the rules and always _____ camper activity.

    A. compromise

    B. infer

    C. monitor

    D. qualify

    E. abbreviate

7. Being _____ and not wasting time while working on a project is *essential* to its success.

    A. urgent

    B. stationary

    C. juvenile

    D. inseparable

    E. efficient

8. Dr. Hastings, who had just graduated, felt some _____ because her very first patient required *urgent* care.

    A. anxiety

    B. fury

    C. hardship

    D. famine

    E. feud

Exercise II – Synonyms and Antonyms

Match the word with its synonym.

1. _____ stationary

2. _____ urgent

3. _____ preserve

4. _____ fury

5. _____ abbreviate

6. _____ reside

7. _____ abide

A. condense

B. rage

C. tolerate

D. critical

E. immobile

F. maintain

G. inhabit

Match the word with its antonym.

8. _____ juvenile

9. _____ inseparable

10. _____ feud

11. _____ anxiety

12. _____ prevailing

13. _____ hideous

14. _____ prosperous

H. weakest

I. confidence

J. divisible

K. peace

L. poor

M. mature

N. delightful

Achieving excellence! On to **Lesson Sixteen**!

Lesson Sixteen

apprehensive
A-PREE-**HEN**-SIV

adj. fearful of the future

The thought of a blizzard coming makes me very *apprehensive*.

syn: anxious; uneasy   *ant: confident*

assemble
AH-**SEM**-BULL

v. to gather together; to put parts together

Marnie *assembled* her best friends to help her decorate her new bedroom.

syn: meet; construct   *ant: leave; separate*

condemn
KUN-**DEM**

v. to judge as unfit or wrong

Do not *condemn* Shelly for forgetting your birthday; I forgot to remind her.

syn: criticize   *ant: praise*

confidential
KAHN-FIH-**DEN**-SHULL

adj. secret or private

What I am about to tell you is *confidential*; you cannot repeat it to anyone.

syn: classified   *ant: public; well known*

disintegrate
DIS-**IN**-TIH-GRAYT

v. to break down completely

A big wave came out of nowhere and *disintegrated* my sand castle!

syn: ruin; rot

hijack
HIY-JAK

v. to steal from or take over, usually by force

While I was taking a nap, Josh *hijacked* my new bike and took it for a ride without my permission.

syn: seize   *ant: return*

patriotism
PAY-TREE-UH-TIZM

n. devotion to one's country

Show your *patriotism* by learning how your government works.

ant: treason

prey

PRAY

n. an animal hunted for food by another animal

Zebras, gazelles, and wild pigs are the usual *prey* for lions.

syn: *quarry*   ant: *hunter; predator*

responsible

REH-**SPAHN**-SIH-BULL

adj. having control over, the care of, or the blame for

The *responsible* chef threw away any food that he thought might be getting old.

syn: *accountable*   ant: *irresponsible*

tenant

TEH-NENT

n. a person who rents a place to live

Tenants of the apartment must pay a monthly rental fee of $1,200.

syn: *occupant; renter*

Exercise I – Words in Context

Using the list of vocabulary words, supply the correct word to complete each sentence.

1. As a spy, John often learns _____ information about people's personal lives.

2. The model rocket took off too quickly and _____ in the air.

3. The Justice Team _____ its strongest, most powerful Superheroes to defeat the giant robot attacking Boston.

4. Many people who enter the US Army think of it as an act of _____.

5. To make a getaway, the criminal _____ an airplane and flew it to Norway.

6. _____ that she would forget her homework, Marcia put reminder notes all over her room.

7. Many _____ complained to the landlord about the broken plumbing.

8. The hungry bear stood above the stream, waiting for some of its _____ to swim by.

9. Dad _____ my older sister for not telling him about the dent on the bumper of the car.

10. The _____ way to drive is to follow all the traffic rules.

Exercise II – Finish the Sentence

First, choose the ending for each sentence that makes the best sense with the italicized vocabulary word used. Then, write your own ending for each sentence that shows you understand the meaning of the vocabulary word.

1. Because I had never been on a motorcycle, I was *apprehensive*…
   A. when my friend asked me to ride on hers.
   B. after my uncle sold his.

2. If you don't keep the birthday party *confidential*,…
   A. it will no longer be a surprise.
   B. all the decorations will look bad.

3. I sure wish that you could be more *responsible* so I…
   A. could have a turn playing video games.
   B. did not have to do all of your chores.

4. *Patriotism* is necessary when…
   A. the president is being investigated for wrongdoing.
   B. a nation needs to be unified in times of war.

5. The *tenants* were happy to…
   A. travel the country in their RV.
   B. pay the rent after the improvements were made.

6. To avoid becoming *prey*, some animals…
   A. camouflage themselves when a large animal is nearby.
   B. hunt for smaller animals to eat.

7. The president spoke on TV and *condemned*…
   A. the soldier for his bravery in battle.
   B. the man who tried to blow up the subway.

8. After he finished *assembling* all the facts, the detective…
   A. determined who had committed the crime and why.
   B. needed to find more evidence to prove his theory.

9. Lee's hopes for the lead part in the play *disintegrated* when…

    A. he realized his favorite teacher was the director.

    B. he messed up his lines during the audition.

10. The men who *hijacked* the jet…

    A. were sent to prison for life.

    B. were just doing their jobs for the airline.

Exercise III – Crossword Puzzle

Use the clues and the words from this lesson to complete the crossword puzzle.

Across

2. After the earthquake, the city government _____ several buildings because they were no longer safe.

4. Having to go to a new school made me nervous and _____.

6. Please be more _____ about money and don't waste it on foolish things.

8. The fire alarm rang, and all the _____ ran outside.

10. Teri won the election, but the results need to be kept _____, so don't tell anyone yet.

Down

1. Every year, leaders from all over the world _____ in Sweden for meetings.

3. A huge meteor lit up the sky as it _____ high in the atmosphere.

5. Coyotes are multiplying in areas that have plentiful _____ such as mice and rabbits.

7. _____ means more than just waving a flag; it means doing what's best for your country.

9. Whenever we're talking, Caleb _____ the conversation and brings up a different subject.

Exercise IV – Critical Reading

Carefully read the passage and then choose the best answer for each of the questions that follow. The passage contains vocabulary words from the lesson.

Soldiers and politicians were the face of the American Revolution. But, as in most wars, many of the major players operated in the shadows, using fake names and identities. They were spies, and without them, the colonies might never have won freedom. These people risked their lives to steal **confidential** information from the

5   British. Two of the war's most important spies were Hercules Mulligan and Cato.

In 1765, Mulligan joined a group called the Sons of Liberty in New York. Opposed to Britain's unfair taxation of Americans, the Sons were one of the first groups to call for independence. In his day job, Mulligan worked as a tailor. When the Revolutionary War began, Mulligan combined his **patriotism** with his work.

10   Some of Mulligan's customers were British soldiers or officers. While in their company, Mulligan pretended to be loyal to Britain. The British thought Mulligan was a friend, so they sometimes discussed their military plans around him. Keeping up his front as a humble tailor, Mulligan **hijacked** any information he could get and passed it on to the Continental Army. Alexander Hamilton, once a **tenant** of Mulligan's

15   property, received Mulligan's stolen secrets.

Historians believe Mulligan might have been **responsible** for saving George Washington's life. One customer had revealed a British plan to capture important American officers. They especially wanted to capture General Washington, which might have ended the war. Mulligan got the information to Washington and spoiled

20   the plan. He also warned Washington of British troop movements, which helped the Continentals prepare for battles or avoid them altogether. For example, Mulligan told Washington the British were planning to go to Delaware in 1777. Washington had time to **assemble** his troops against the attack.

Mulligan's success was made possible by Cato. Also a patriot, Cato carried

25   messages between Mulligan and the American troops. The British did not suspect Cato because he was an African American slave. This allowed him to move through British areas easily. Without Cato, the Continental Army might never have received the information Hercules Mulligan had gathered.

Unfortunately, Mulligan and Cato eventually ran out of luck. The British had

30   suspicions about Cato, so they put him in prison and beat him. After Cato's release, the pair were more careful about how they delivered messages. Mulligan, too, was imprisoned, but the British were unable to prove he was a spy. He could have been **condemned** to death for treason.

Determined to beat the British, Cato and Mulligan continued to spy until the end

35   of the war. General Washington personally thanked them for their help. Today, their story reminds us that a war that changed the course of history was won not only by cannons and soldiers, but by a slave and a tailor.

Exercise IV – Critical Reading Questions

1. Choose the best title for this passage.
    A. Cato and Mulligan: Hidden Soldiers
    B. General Washington's Assistants
    C. Spies of the American Revolution
    D. Colonial American Clothing
    E. Prisons During the American Revolution

2. What is the main purpose of paragraph 3?
    A. to explain Cato's role in the operation
    B. to describe General Washington's plan
    C. to inform the reader about British troop movements
    D. to describe the way Mulligan gathered information
    E. to discuss Mulligan's background in New York

3. As it is used in line 13, *front* most nearly means
    A. movement.
    B. assignment.
    C. requirement.
    D. volunteering.
    E. disguise.

4. Choose the statement with which the author would most likely agree.
    A. One or two people are capable of changing the world.
    B. Hercules Mulligan was never a traitor.
    C. Cato and Mulligan worked for honor, not the cause of the Revolution.
    D. George Washington did not appreciate Hercules Mulligan enough.
    E. The British were right to fight the colonists.

5. Choose the sentence from the passage that best supports your answer to the previous question.
    A. "Opposed to Britain's unfair taxation of Americans, the Sons were one of the first groups to call for independence." (lines 7-8)
    B. "He also warned Washington of British troop movements, which helped the Continentals prepare for battles or avoid them altogether." (lines 20-21)
    C. "Without Cato, the Continental Army might never have received the information Hercules Mulligan had gathered." (lines 27-28)
    D. "The British had suspicions about Cato, so they put him in prison and beat him." (lines 29-30)
    E. "Today, their story reminds us that a war that changed the course of history was won not only by cannons and soldiers, but by a slave and a tailor." (lines 35-37)

Superior effort!
On to **Lesson
Seventeen**!

Lesson Seventeen

abundant
A-**BUN**-DENT

adj. present in a large amount

Flowers are *abundant* in the Stevensons' beautiful garden out back.

syn: plentiful   *ant: rare; scarce*

adolescent
A-DUH-**LEH**-SENT

n. a person between childhood and adulthood

Hallie could go to the movies without a parent now that she was an *adolescent*.

syn: juvenile; teenager

dwell
DWEL

v. to live or stay in a place or in a certain mental state

The family of trolls *dwells* under the green bridge.

syn: inhabit   *ant: move*

gauge
GAYJ

v. to measure or to estimate something

I could not *gauge* exactly how much food the bearded dragon would eat, so I bought a pound.

syn: determine

hygiene
HIY-JEEN

n. a practice that aids good health

To keep up good *hygiene*, you should floss your teeth every day.

ant: dirtiness

impractical
IM-**PRAK**-TIH-KULL

adj. not useful or worth the effort

Wearing sandals for a hiking trip would be very *impractical*.

syn: unrealistic   *ant: sensible*

irritate
EER-IH-TAYT

v. to make annoyed or impatient

Mosquito bites will usually *irritate* me for days.

syn: bother   *ant: soothe*

modesty
MAH-DIH-STEE

n. a lack of excess pride

Showing *modesty* is much nicer than some people think it is.

syn: humility   *ant: bragging*

outlandish
OWT-**LAND**-ISH

adj. especially strange

The safari explorer has had many *outlandish* adventures, including riding a rhino.

syn: bizarre   *ant: normal; ordinary*

sanitary
SAN-IH-TER-EE

adj. free of filth or germs harmful to health

Please wash your hands after you use the restroom so that the restaurant stays *sanitary*.

syn: sterile   *ant: dirty*

Exercise I – Words in Context

Using the list of vocabulary words, supply the correct word to complete each sentence.

1. Maddie would be considered a[n] _____ because she has just started high school.

2. You can notice Melanie's _____ by the way she politely accepts compliments.

3. Stopping at roadside detours is fun but _____ if you want to get to your destination on time.

4. I enjoy sunshine, but too much humidity _____ me.

5. I would not eat food that fell on the floor because it is not _____.

6. I could not _____ how happy Eleni was because she rarely shows any emotions.

7. Sand is _____ everywhere in the desert, but water is not.

8. I take my dog to the park so often that people probably think he _____ there.

9. My grandfather tells me many _____ tales of his childhood that I find hard to believe.

10. Mike showers only once a week, which is just bad _____.

Exercise II – Finish the Sentence

First, choose the ending for each sentence that makes the best sense with the italicized vocabulary word used. Then, write your own ending for each sentence that shows you understand the meaning of the vocabulary word.

1. Harry's choice of *outlandish* clothing and shoes revealed…
   A. that he likes plain clothing.
   B. his need to be noticed by people.

2. For the wedding, *abundant*…
   A. flowers were displayed all around the chapel.
   B. rings were placed next to each other on a small pillow.

3. This equipment must be kept *sanitary*, or…
   A. patients could become infected.
   B. the metal could be damaged.

4. Setting the air conditioner to 60 degrees is *impractical* because…
   A. it is a good temperature for keeping people cool.
   B. some employees will have to wear sweaters during summer.

5. Jerell's *modesty* prevents him from…
   A. keeping quiet about how much money his dad makes.
   B. telling people about the award he won.

6. In spite of his good *hygiene*, Calvin…
   A. still caught the flu.
   B. was late for work.

7. If you keep acting like an *adolescent*,…
   A. Mom will keep treating you like a kid, even though you're twenty-two.
   B. none of the younger cousins will think you are fun to play with.

8. Don't *dwell* on the bad parts of the movie; you need to…
   A. focus on how original the story was.
   B. recognize that this was not a very good film.

9. The polls before the election tried to *gauge*…

    A. undecided voters to participate in the election.

    B. what percentage of people would vote for each candidate.

10. What *irritates* me most about bedtime is that…

    A. my mom usually reads me a story.

    B. it is way too early for me.

Exercise III – Crossword Puzzle

Use the clues and the words from this lesson to complete the crossword puzzle.

Across

2. Marnie is very smart, but has no _____ and always brags about her perfect grades.

4. In the lab, _____ conditions are needed so as not to spoil the experiments.

5. The _____ puppy still had some growing up to do.

9. It's just _____ to believe in Bigfoot or UFOs because there has never been any proof of either one.

10. Few people _____ me more than Zander does; he talks too much.

Down

1. My motorcycle is _____ for bringing groceries home.

3. Over the course of months, the spy _____ the readiness of the country's army to fight off an invasion.

6. Hank is usually frowning, and anger seems to _____ inside him.

7. The red corrections were so _____ on my paper that I could barely read what I had typed.

8. Better _____ will prevent illnesses like the flu from spreading.

Exercise IV – Critical Reading

Carefully read the passage and then choose the best answer for each of the questions that follow. The passage contains vocabulary words from the lesson.

Wild fish used to be **abundant** in the ocean. However, a worldwide demand for seafood has led to the disappearance of some saltwater species. To meet the demand, companies now raise and harvest fish using a farming technique known as aquaculture. Most fish farms feature huge indoor tanks that can hold thousands of
5   individuals. Other farms keep fish contained in pens or underwater cages anchored to the banks of rivers and lakes. Although aquaculture has reduced the overharvesting of wild fish, some people believe standard aquaculture methods are bad for the environment. Current methods create too much waste, damage small waterways, and spread disease among the fish stocks and native wildlife. One inventor, Steve Page,
10   has proposed a solution to aquaculture's problems. He helped create the Aquapod, a system that moves fish farms from land to the world's oceans.

Aquapods are large, golf-ball shaped structures that float freely beneath the ocean's surface in deeper water. They are made from recycled plastic. Each plastic section is in the shape of a triangle, and all these panels connect to make the round
15   ball shape. Some are nearly 100 feet in diameter. The panels are covered with brass netting, protecting the fish stock from predators that **dwell** in the sea, such as sharks, dolphins, and sea lions. Since Aquapods are not held down by anchors or ropes, they are easily transported all over the world with the help of the ocean's currents.

Different kinds of fish can live their full, natural lives in Aquapods. A single large
20   Aquapod can hold tens of thousands of fish at a time. The fish have plenty of room to swim around in large social groups, a behavior known as shoaling (schooling). In traditional fish farm tanks, overcrowding leads to stress, disease, and even death among the fish. The Aquapod is designed to prevent all these things from happening. It allows fish to live freely in their natural environment.

25   Aquapods also attract other creatures. Some wild fish and sea creatures gather near the Aquapods. In some ways, Aquapods are like artificial coral reefs. They provide new homes for many different sea creatures. Because large amounts of water pass through the Aquapod, most of the fish waste flows back into the ocean, where smaller creatures, like plankton and shrimp, eat it. This is much more **sanitary** than
30   land aquaculture, where waste builds up at the bottom of the tanks, which sickens fish and pollutes local water sources.

Page thinks that traditional fish farming cannot work as it currently does. He believes that it will only harm the environment, not help it. The only way to save the environment and grow seafood is to place fish farms out in the deep ocean. The idea
35   might seem **outlandish**, but it could be the only way to sustain our fish supply and waterways.

Exercise IV – Critical Reading Questions

1. The main purpose of this passage is to
   A. convince readers to buy less seafood.
   B. explain why aquaculture is necessary to produce seafood.
   C. argue that Aquapods are the best way to farm fish.
   D. inform readers about the dangers of eating traditionally farmed fish.
   E. describe how fish live inside of an Aquapod.

2. As it is used in line 5, the word *pen* most nearly means
   A. ocean.
   B. marker.
   C. ship.
   D. enclosure.
   E. tank.

3. In addition to reducing pollution from fish farms, how else does the use of Aquapods reduce waste?
   A. Aquapods do not spread diseases to freshwater creatures.
   B. Aquapods are made of recycled materials.
   C. Using Aquapods is more practical than growing fish in a tank.
   D. Aquapods can grow a lot of fish in a small space.
   E. Aquapods can be used at locations around the world.

4. Which of the following lines best supports your answer to question 3?
   A. "Aquapods are large, golf-ball shaped structures…made from recycled plastic." (lines 12-13)
   B. "The panels are covered with brass netting, protecting the fish stock from predators that dwell in the sea…" (lines 15-16)
   C. "A single large Aquapod can hold tens of thousands of fish at a time." (lines 19-20)
   D. "In some ways, Aquapods are like artificial coral reefs." (line 26)
   E. "The Aquapod is designed to prevent all these things from happening." (line 23)

5. The author of this passage would most likely agree with which statement?
   A. Aquapods are not needed because people do not eat a lot of seafood.
   B. Traditional fish farming cannot last forever.
   C. Aquapods are too expensive to produce and sell.
   D. Using Aquapods probably will not help save the environment.
   E. Traditional fish farming is the best way to raise fish.

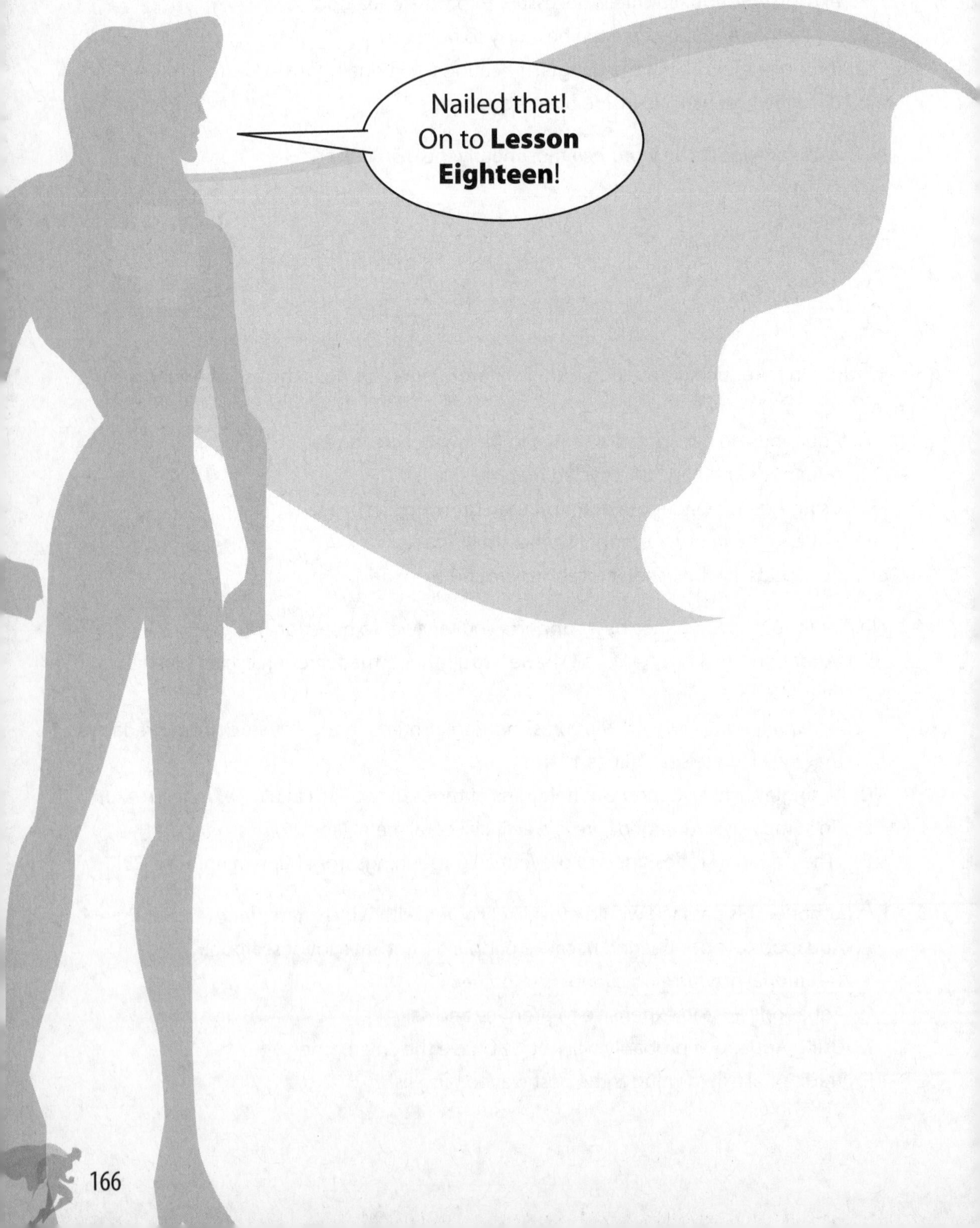
Nailed that!
On to **Lesson Eighteen**!

Lesson Eighteen

ail
AYL

v. to cause pain or sickness

The giraffe hadn't moved all morning, and its keeper wondered what *ailed* it.

syn: bother; distress   *ant: ease*

depart
DIH-**PART**

v. to go away

The cruise ship will *depart* from the dock at around 2:00 p.m.

syn: leave; exit   *ant: arrive; enter*

enterprise
EN-TUR-PRIYZ

n. a long, difficult project or business venture

Mom quit her old job to work full time in her new business *enterprise*.

syn: endeavor; operation

frank
FRANK

adj. direct and honest

I will be *frank* with you; your mustache looks very silly.

syn: sincere   *ant: dishonest; phony*

frequent
FREE-KWENT

adj. happening often

Janie is such a *frequent* customer that the storeowner knows her name.

syn: regular   *ant: occasional*

manufacture
MAN-YOO-FAK-SHUR

v. to make a product, usually in large amounts

This factory *manufactures* the sneakers that our basketball team uses.

syn: produce

peculiar
PEH-**KYOOL**-YER

adj. unique and unusual

To Grant, who had grown up in Florida, the snowstorm was a *peculiar* sight.

syn: odd; strange   *ant: ordinary; usual*

spectacle

SPEK-TIH-KULL

n. a large, public display or performance, often very showy or shocking

The lights of Paris seen from the top of the Eiffel Tower at night are quite a *spectacle*.

syn: marvel; wonder

sympathy

SIMP-IH-THEE

n. the sharing of sadness or emotional pain felt by another

Our family expresses *sympathy* for the loss of your great-grandmother.

syn: pity; compassion   ant: indifference

toll

TOHL

n. money paid for use of a service, especially passage on a bridge or road

We are about to enter the highway; do you have change to pay the *toll*?

syn: fee; charge

Exercise I – Words in Context

Using the list of vocabulary words, supply the correct word to complete each sentence.

1. You have my _____ ; it sounds like your day was really terrible.

2. It would be _____ for a teenager to still believe in Santa Claus.

3. Jeremy spoke in a[n] _____ manner, telling the group exactly how he felt about the loss of money.

4. Edison made a[n] _____ of himself when he began to sing in the middle of the hallway.

5. The patient had been _____ for months until a new doctor prescribed a better medicine.

6. Check to make sure you have packed everything you need before we _____ for the airport.

7. If we exit the highway now, will we avoid paying the _____?

8. Leonardo knows which rides will have the shortest lines, since he is a[n] _____ visitor to the amusement park.

9. Dorothy's big _____ involves opening five new locations for her restaurant chain.

10. The easiest way to _____ more toy trucks each day was to install robots that could put them together faster.

Exercise II – Finish the Sentence

First, choose the ending for each sentence that makes the best sense with the italicized vocabulary word used. Then, write your own ending for each sentence that shows you understand the meaning of the vocabulary word.

1. *Frequent* stops while hiking made…
   A. the five-mile trip take longer than expected.
   B. me feel too tired to continue walking.

2. The *peculiar* box sitting on the side of the road…
   A. was something you were likely to see all the time.
   B. startled the soldier because it might contain an explosive device.

3. Please give me a *frank*…
   A. amount of money so I can buy the groceries.
   B. opinion on what you thought about that book.

4. Rarely has history witnessed an *enterprise* as vast and bold as…
   A. the US government's space program.
   B. taking selfies with cellphone cameras.

5. The fireworks *spectacle*…
   A. was completely boring to me and my friends.
   B. lasted for an hour and cost over $1 million.

6. Patricia had no *sympathy* for the wealthy businessman who…
   A. could not afford a private jet.
   B. had lost his spouse to cancer, just as she had.

7. We didn't mind the *toll* because…
   A. we were in a hurry to get to the city.
   B. it did not cost very much.

8. Fixing what is *ailing* the oceans will…
   A. require cleaning up pollution.
   B. mean that ships should be built larger.

9. It was hard to *manufacture* a lot of computers because…

    A. Brian did not know computer programming.

    B. Brian's company owned only one small factory.

10. As soon as we *departed* from the city,…

    A. traffic worsened as drivers headed downtown.

    B. the air seemed fresher and the nights quieter.

Exercise III – Crossword Puzzle

Use the clues and the words from this lesson to complete the crossword puzzle.

Across

4. Mia's family _____ had been founded by her grandparents, and most of her siblings worked in the business.

6. The police officer spoke to us in a[n] _____ way, pointing out the dangers and effects of drug abuse.

7. Elle said to Chloe, "Reading the chapter from back to front is a[n] _____ way to study."

8. Dina used to have _____ headaches until she realized that chocolate was the cause, so she stopped eating it.

9. Sharon was in the hospital room for ten minutes before she showed any _____ for our sick aunt.

Down

1. Elon Musk _____ electric cars that run without using gasoline.

2. One colorful _____ we saw in Hawaii was the red lava flowing into the ocean.

3. The whole family couldn't wait to _____ for their island vacation.

5. The highway was turned into a[n] _____-free road to speed up traffic.

10. "Whatever _____ you, these copper bracelets will cure it," the salesman claimed, but we didn't believe him.

Exercise IV – Improving Paragraphs

Carefully read the passage and then choose the best answer for each of the questions. The questions will ask you to make changes to improve the writing of the passage.

1   [1] The sun would feel much worse if not for a part of the atmosphere called the "ozone layer." [2] The ozone layer blocks out ultraviolet (UV) rays from the sun. [3] UV rays damage the DNA in cells that make up your body. [4] The UV rays that make it to Earth are enough to cause sunburn and even skin cancer. [5] They also cause cold food to spoil or melt. [6] Without the ozone, life couldn't survive on Earth. [7] That is why scientists were very worried when they found a weak spot in the ozone layer. [8] What could be causing it? {1}

2   In 1985, scientists noticed a gap in the ozone layer above Antarctica. They realized that a scientific report from 1974 was correct when it stated that Chlorofluorocarbons (CFCs) are harmful to the ozone. CFCs at the time were used to pressurize products in spray cans {2} such as paint hairspray and deodorant. CFCs were also important in **manufacturing** air conditioning units. For years, CFC gases rose high in the atmosphere and destroyed ozone particles, putting a hole in Earth's protective cover. The hole varies in size; its weakest spot reappears around August of each year.

3   Since 1985, most countries have banned the **frequent** use of CFCs. Several countries agreed to stop using them when the Montreal Protocol passed in 1987. The protocol now includes bans on other chemicals that harm the environment.

4   [1] Small amounts of CFCs are still used in some appliances but not enough to be harmful. [2] Since they were banned, damage to the ozone layer has stopped. [3] Damage to the ozone has slowed down since the Montreal Protocol. [4] Recently, scientists have observed that the hole is shrinking. [5] It used to be over 4.5 million square miles. [6] It is now 1.5 million square miles. [7] The weak spot forms later in the year and lasts for a shorter amount of time than it used to. [8] Scientists say that the ozone has healed because there are fewer CFCs in the atmosphere, making the Montreal Protocol a success. {3} {4} {5}

Exercise IV – Improving Paragraphs Questions

1. One of the sentences in paragraph 1 contributes nothing to the main idea. Choose the sentence that should be deleted.
   A. sentence 2
   B. sentence 3
   C. sentence 5
   D. sentence 6

2. The underlined portion of the sentence contains an error. Choose the best way to correct it.

   "CFCs at the time were used to pressurize products in spray cans <u>such as paint hairspray and deodorant</u>."

   A. such as paint and hairspray and deodorant
   B. with paint, hairspray and deodorant
   C. such as paint with hairspray and deodorant
   D. such as paint, hairspray, and deodorant

3. Which sentence in paragraph 4 should be removed because it repeats an idea that has already been stated?
   A. sentence 1
   B. sentence 3
   C. sentence 4
   D. sentence 5

4. The writer wants to add the following sentence to the passage:

   "The summer sun sometimes feels so hot that all you want to do is sit inside all day."

   Choose the point at which the sentence should be inserted.
   A. the beginning of paragraph 1
   B. the end of paragraph 1
   C. the beginning of paragraph 4
   D. the end of paragraph 4

5. If the writer wanted to make the passage longer, what would be a good topic to discuss at the end of the passage?
   A. the types of sprays that work better than CFCs
   B. advancements in skin cancer research
   C. how the ozone layer could be protected in the future
   D. the history of weather systems around Antarctica

Review: Lessons 16-18

Exercise I – Related Words

Choose the word that best completes the sentence.

1. Because of his *modesty*, Felipe was _____ about discussing his award on television.
   A. responsible
   B. frequent
   C. apprehensive
   D. impractical
   E. outlandish

2. Sean's factory _____ remote-control cars that came with *abundant* special features like tires that never wore out.
   A. disintegrated
   B. gauged
   C. irritated
   D. departed
   E. manufactured

3. Mara's three barking puppies *irritated* all the _____ in her apartment building.
   A. adolescents
   B. tenants
   C. tolls
   D. sympathies
   E. spectacles

4. The blindfolded clown who was juggling flaming rings was the most *outlandish* _____ at the carnival.
   A. hygiene
   B. tenant
   C. adolescent
   D. spectacle
   E. patriotism

5. The _____ tone of the FBI agent's voice proved that he was serious about not revealing the *confidential* code to anyone.

    A. frank

    B. sanitary

    C. peculiar

    D. impractical

    E. frequent

6. Keep the kitchen *sanitary* by maintaining good _____ and washing your hands often.

    A. hygiene

    B. modesty

    C. patriotism

    D. sympathy

    E. toll

7. We asked a[n] _____ adult to *gauge* how safe the old bicycle was.

    A. confidential

    B. outlandish

    C. abundant

    D. responsible

    E. impractical

8. The homeless shelter counted on many *frequent* volunteers who _____ there every Sunday afternoon to prepare food in the kitchen.

    A. dwelled

    B. assembled

    C. hijacked

    D. condemned

    E. irritated

Exercise II – Synonyms and Antonyms

Match the word with its synonym.

1. _____ condemn

A. inhabit

2. _____ sanitary

B. determine

3. _____ dwell

C. humility

4. _____ peculiar

D. criticize

5. _____ modesty

E. strange

6. _____ sympathy

F. sterile

7. _____ gauge

G. compassion

Match the word with its antonym.

8. _____ confidential

H. leave

9. _____ apprehensive

I. scarce

10. _____ assemble

J. sensible

11. _____ abundant

K. public

12. _____ impractical

L. occasional

13. _____ frequent

M. ordinary

14. _____ outlandish

N. confident

Lesson Nineteen

abode
UH-**BOHD**

n. the place or shelter in which someone lives

"Welcome to my *abode*!" I said, as I opened the door wide for my party guests.

syn: home; dwelling

analyze
AN-UH-LIYZ

v. to study in close detail

The scientist *analyzed* her data and noticed a strange pattern in the numbers.

syn: examine; inspect

artifact
AR-TIH-FAKT

n. a man-made object from an earlier time

The watch my cousin found is actually an *artifact* from a Civil War battlefield.

syn: relic

endanger
EN-**DAYN**-JUR

v. to put in a dangerous situation

Letting the campfire burn after you leave *endangers* the whole community.

syn: risk; jeopardize   *ant: protect*

grieve
GREEV

v. to experience great sorrow, especially over loss

Farrah *grieved* over the career-ending injury to her favorite figure skater.

syn: mourn   *ant: celebrate; rejoice*

merge
MURJ

v. to join two things together

My band *merges* rock music with folk music for a unique sound.

syn: combine; blend   *ant: divide; separate*

offensive
UH-**FEN**-SIV

adj. causing anger or upset

Jeff's comment that boys play sports better than girls do was *offensive* to Leslie.

syn: disgusting; horrible   *ant: pleasant; respectful*

symptom

SIMP-TUM

n. a sign that something exists or is happening

A high fever is one of the many *symptoms* of the flu.

syn: evidence; indication

vague

VAYG

adj. unclear; not wholly communicated

I have a *vague* idea of how your trip went, but could you give me more details?

syn: uncertain   *ant: definite*

wholesome

HOHL-SUM

adj. good for moral or physical health

Mr. Kelin worries that playing violent videogames is not a *wholesome* activity for his children.

syn: respectable   *ant: impure*

Exercise I – Words in Context

Using the list of vocabulary words, supply the correct word to complete each sentence.

1. Brittany used a magnifying glass to _____ pollen on the bees' legs to see what kinds of flowers they were visiting.

2. I have only a[n] _____ memory of Aunt Lila because the last time I saw her, I was four years old.

3. Songs written specifically for G-rated movies are usually very _____.

4. The museum Sam visited displayed many _____ from an old Greek village.

5. "You seem healthy, but let me know if you develop _____ like a sore throat or headache," said Dr. Briggs.

6. The active volcano _____ everyone living within thirty miles of it.

7. It was sad when my parents decided to sell our old _____ and move us into a new one.

8. The head chef _____ when his assistant dropped the cake they had spent all weekend preparing.

9. The reporter spoke negatively about the film, calling it "_____ to anyone who paid to see it."

10. The three fifth-grade classes _____ together for their field trip to the museum.

Exercise II – Finish the Sentence

First, choose the ending for each sentence that makes the best sense with the italicized vocabulary word used. Then, write your own ending for each sentence that shows you understand the meaning of the vocabulary word.

1. You were *offensive* when you wrote…

    A. mean comments in your classmate's yearbook.

    B. an email in which you apologized to a friend.

2. Don't give me any *vague* answers; I need…

    A. a general idea of how you feel.

    B. to know exactly what to do.

3. You should eat unprocessed, *wholesome* food because…

    A. it will be less enjoyable for you.

    B. it is healthier for you than junk food is.

4. I won the auction for an *artifact* that…

    A. was made before the Pilgrims landed in America.

    B. was worth over a hundred dollars.

5. The four-year-old's short temper and crying fits were *symptoms* of…

    A. not getting enough sleep last night.

    B. things she had drawn with crayons yesterday.

6. The island had once been the *abode* of seals, but…

    A. there are dozens of them on the beach.

    B. they have left, in search of more fish.

7. My mom still *grieves* for her favorite dog that…

    A. died suddenly last spring.

    B. always wants to play outside.

8. One bad grade on a test can *endanger*…

    A. your chances of getting into college.

    B. your perfect A average.

9. The cars in all lanes need to *merge* because…

    A. the road narrows to a single lane ahead.

    B. the traffic light has turned red.

10. Colin *analyzed* his mistake, but…

    A. he could not figure out exactly where he went wrong.

    B. he didn't really put much thought into it.

Exercise III – Crossword Puzzle

Use the clues and the words from this lesson to complete the crossword puzzle.

Across

2. Don't _____ , Stephen; we'll get another fish to replace Goldie.

6. For question seven, you need to _____ the information to figure out what percent of families have more than five children.

7. "One more _____ comment about my cooking, and you can go feed yourself!"

9. The only _____ I have from my ancestors' time in China is an ancient-looking wooden pair of shoes.

10. They advertised the butter as "_____ and containing no artificial colors or flavors."

Down

1. Gradually, the two cartoon figures began to _____ into each other to create a new superhero.

3. Stay on the path, or you will _____ the delicate plants and creatures that live along the nature trail.

4. Failing this simple test is a[n] _____ of your poor study habits.

5. The company executive's beautiful _____ stood high up in the hills, away from the homes below it.

8. Be more exact because your answer about Jefferson was too _____ .

Exercise IV – Critical Reading

Carefully read the passage and then choose the best answer for each of the questions that follow. The passage contains vocabulary words from the lesson.

In 1922, Lady Evelyn Herbert received an invitation from her father, Lord Carnarvon, to travel with him to Egypt. Carnarvon had been paying for archaeologist Howard Carter's attempts to find King Tutankhamun's tomb. After seven years of searching, Carter believed that he had located the pharaoh's final **abode**. He wanted
5   Carnarvon to join him when he opened the tomb.

Lord Carnarvon and Lady Evelyn arrived at the site in Luxor, Egypt, on November 23, 1922. Carter and his team had already found stairs and a passageway leading to the tomb. In the process, Carter realized that they would not be the tomb's first visitors. Broken stones indicated that grave robbers had entered long before. The
10 team **analyzed** the hieroglyphics on a sealed door at the end of the corridor. Carter breached the door just enough to peek inside the next room. He inserted a lit candle to test for bad air that could **endanger** the team.

Carter peered through the hole. He saw glimmering gold items and other ancient **artifacts**. The team entered the room, moving carefully to avoid further damage to the
15 tomb. When Lady Evelyn joined Carter, she was the first woman to enter the tomb in over 3,000 years! Evelyn and her father explored the new chamber. They found two sealed doors. One led to a small room containing more treasures. Carter was sure the other door led to the burial chamber. The team explored the room for weeks before opening the final door. There, the riches of the ancient boy-king surrounded a heavy,
20 gold coffin in which King Tutankhamun had slept for thousands of years.

The discovery of Tut's mummy captured the world's attention and inspired "Tutmania." Newspapers everywhere featured the discovery. Fashion, architecture, and even dancing, for a while, were not trendy unless they referred to Egypt, treasure, or King Tut. Sadly, Lord Carnarvon and Lady Evelyn did not get to enjoy
25 the craze. Eleven days after the opening of the burial chamber, Lord Carnarvon felt ill. He went to the Egyptian city of Aswan to rest. During that time, a mosquito bit him on the face. He then went on to nick the bite while shaving. The tiny wound became infected, which caused a fever. Lady Evelyn looked after her father, but his **symptoms** became worse. On April 5, 1923, Lord Carnarvon died. Rumors arose that
30 Carnarvon was a victim of Tut's curse—punishment for having disturbed the tomb. The rumors were unfounded, however, because the other explorers, including Lady Evelyn and Howard Carter, remained healthy for decades.

Exercise IV – Critical Reading Questions

1. The main focus of this passage is
    A. how scientists and treasure hunters explore tombs
    B. the people involved with the discovery of Tut's tomb
    C. the life and death of King Tut
    D. how Evelyn became the first woman in Tut's tomb
    E. ancient Egyptian mummies

2. As it is used in line 11, the word *breached* most nearly means
    A. crawled under.
    B. dusted off.
    C. checked out.
    D. broke through.
    E. used explosives on.

3. What clue indicated that grave robbers had entered King Tut's tomb?
    A. There were pieces of broken stone by the entrance.
    B. Almost all of the expected treasure had been stolen.
    C. The burial chamber had been opened.
    D. The mummy of King Tut was missing.
    E. A hole had been carved in the stone door.

4. Choose the statement that the writer would most likely agree with.
    A. Everyone knew about Carter's discovery of Tut's tomb.
    B. King Tut's tomb should have been left alone.
    C. Carter's team should have sold artifacts for profit.
    D. Explorers must be aware of ancient curses.
    E. The discovery of Tut's tomb went largely unnoticed.

5. Choose the line from the passage that best supports your answer to the previous question.
    A. "Carter and his team had already found stairs and a passageway leading to the tomb." (lines 7-8)
    B. "The team explored the room for weeks before opening the final door." (lines 18-19)
    C. "The discovery of Tut's mummy captured the world's attention and inspired 'Tutmania.'" (lines 21-22)
    D. "The tiny wound became infected, which caused a fever." (lines 27-28)
    E. "…the other explorers, including Lady Evelyn and Howard Carter, remained healthy for decades." (lines 31-32)

Excellent effort!
On to **Lesson
Twenty**!

Lesson Twenty

acquire
AH-**KWIYR**

v. to gain ownership of

To *acquire* any learned skill, you must first practice a great deal.

syn: obtain

diagram
DIY-UH-GRAM

n. an image or drawing that explains how something works

On Matt's *diagram* of the new playground, we counted three sliding boards.

syn: blueprint

expel
EX-**PEL**

v. to drive out with force; to discharge

Many people don't know it, but our bodies *expel* sweat through pores in our skin.

syn: eject

monarch
MAH-NARK

n. the ruler of an empire or kingdom, often through family ties

The Livingstons are a family of *monarchs*; they have ruled Elbonia for the last 122 years.

syn: king; queen; emperor

omnivore
OM-NIH-VOR

n. an animal that eats both meat and plants

Humans are *omnivores*, but some people prefer vegetables over meat.

reprimand
REP-RIH-MAND

v. to scold formally or officially

Ms. Magellan *reprimands* her students when they arrive late to class.

syn: criticize   *ant: praise; honor*

rural
RUR-ULL

adj. pertaining to country life

This *rural* town is full of dirt roads and a great deal of farmland.

syn: rustic   *ant: urban*

spiritual
SPEER-IT-CHOO-ULL

adj. relating to religion or things beyond the physical world

The tribe's *spiritual* activities involve traditional songs and dances.

sufficient
SUH-**FIH**-SHENT

adj. having the needed amount

The bowl of plain pasta was a *sufficient* meal, but it was really nothing special.

syn: adequate; enough　　*ant: lacking*

superior
SOO-**PEER**-EE-UR

adj. higher in rank, quality, or value

Ryan, a *superior* swimmer, had won his race by more than five seconds.

syn: better; extraordinary　　*ant: inferior*

Exercise I – Words in Context

Using the list of vocabulary words, supply the correct word to complete each sentence.

1. The _____ showing how water in clouds becomes rain had pictures that explained each part.

2. Will the principal _____ Becky from school for having spray-painted the teachers' lounge?

3. The tractors and farmhouses were signs that we were entering a[n] _____ area.

4. Five pounds of wood will be _____ to make two birdhouses.

5. Chimpanzees do not eat only bananas; they are _____ and eat small mammals, too.

6. If I were a[n] _____, my first decree would be to ban homework forever.

7. Through forty years of hard work, Malena slowly _____ enough money to retire.

8. Officer Lawrence _____ the boys for throwing snowballs at his car.

9. That 50-inch TV is _____ to the 70-inch model because it has a clearer picture.

10. My uncle likes to light scented candles in his house, giving his place a[n] _____ feel.

Exercise II – Finish the Sentence

First, choose the ending for each sentence that makes the best sense with the italicized vocabulary word used. Then, write your own ending for each sentence that shows you understand the meaning of the vocabulary word.

1. He came from *rural* Oklahoma where he…
    A. worked on his father's ranch.
    B. drove the city bus every evening.

2. My older brother read a *spiritual* novel about…
    A. a dragon that steals the king's crown.
    B. a woman who is saved by an angel.

3. To prove which player had the *superior* ability,…
    A. each quarterback threw the ball to test his accuracy.
    B. the coach said that Mark never missed practice.

4. There wasn't *sufficient* snow to…
    A. build a decent-sized snowman.
    B. use the sidewalks; we needed snowshoes.

5. The family of the person who is now the *monarch* of that country…
    A. no longer wants to be associated with him.
    B. recently moved into the palace.

6. Bears are *omnivores*, so…
    A. be sure to safely store your burgers and chips while camping.
    B. zookeepers feed them a diet of only meat.

7. Without a *diagram*, the students…
    A. will have to miss lunch today.
    B. could not point to all the parts of the flower.

8. Nick was *reprimanded* because he…
    A. didn't wish Michael a happy birthday.
    B. was late for school for the 3rd time.

9. Reading thousands of books has allowed Edith to *acquire*…

    A. a great deal of knowledge.

    B. many trips to the mall over the years.

10. Please *expel* your gum…

    A. and share it with the class.

    B. into the trashcan.

Exercise III – Crossword Puzzle

Use the clues and the words from this lesson to complete the crossword puzzle.

Across

1. Gertrude, the absolute _____ of Planet Zerks, ruled for hundreds of years.

3. Marcus gets good grades, but why does he have to act like he's _____ to everyone else?

5. My sleeping bag was barely _____ to keep my feet warm, and I shivered all night.

7. Before building the drone, Aubrey's father made a[n] _____ that showed the steps involved.

8. Don't count on good cell phone reception way out in the _____ parts of the state.

9. My friend Lucas collects keychains; he has more than fifty and wants to _____ more.

Down

2. The master chef thought the best way to _____ his assistants was to yell at them until they cried.

4. To tell if an animal is a[n] _____, you need to see if it has both sharp and flat teeth.

5. The religion claimed to know the correct path to _____ development.

6. The rattlesnake had bitten the bear five times already and couldn't _____ any more venom from its fangs.

Exercise IV – Critical Reading

Carefully read the passage and then choose the best answer for each of the questions that follow. The passage contains vocabulary words from the lesson.

If intelligence is a super power, then Sherlock Holmes might be the first superhero. Readers in 1887 had not seen anything like him until Arthur Conan Doyle's first book was published. Sherlock is so observant that just a few glances at a crime scene is enough for him to solve a case. Holmes's powers made a favorite
5 genre—the mystery novel—even more fun to read. However, his ability to solve cases that stumped the police was not entirely made-up. Arthur Conan Doyle had a source of real inspiration when he created London's most famous detective.

When Doyle was a medical student in Scotland, he met Dr. Joseph Bell who was a well-known professor and physician. Dr. Bell was the personal doctor of England's
10 famous **monarch** Queen Victoria. To **acquire** the skills to become a doctor, Doyle watched Bell at work and became his assistant at the Edinburgh Royal Infirmary.

Dr. Bell did not rely on textbooks and **diagrams** of the human body to figure out difficult cases. He observed patients closely and looked for clues as to what might be making them sick. After years of practice, Bell was able to deduce personal
15 details about people simply by looking at them. For example, Bell could determine someone's job just by looking at his or her hands, or tell where a sailor had been by noticing any tattoos. With just a glance, Bell could tell where a person lived and how much money he or she had.

Bell's abilities made him a **superior** doctor. He became famous as a professor,
20 teaching his methods to younger generations. Eventually, Bell caught the attention of police detectives who needed help with their cases. In 1888, he was called to investigate the Jack the Ripper murders in London. Police efforts had not been **sufficient** enough to catch the murderer, who had already killed five people. After a week of investigation, Bell wrote down his findings and named a suspect. His notes,
25 however, went missing. The killer was never found.

Arthur Conan Doyle was impressed by Bell's ability to notice details that anyone else would miss. He used Dr. Bell as a model for his character Sherlock Holmes. He gave Sherlock many of his old professor's features, including his walk, his face, his hobbies, and even some of his clothing—especially the long coat and cap with front
30 and back brims. Sherlock Holmes is not a doctor like Bell, though. He's a detective-for-hire who helps solve cases the police cannot. Bell was first a doctor and a professor; detective work was rare for him.

Sherlock Holmes also liked to spend more time alone than the real Dr. Bell, who had a wife and children. Holmes is often unfriendly to other people and **reprimands**
35 them when they don't understand him. Holmes, in fact, stops speaking when he is busy solving problems. He even locks himself inside his apartment at 221B Baker Street until he has a breakthrough. Dr. Watson, his sidekick, is one of his only friends because they work well together.

The Sherlock Holmes adventures were a source of pride for Dr. Bell. He knew
40 that Holmes had a far greater intellect than he did, but he still appreciated the character. Bell continued to work as a professor and doctor in Edinburgh until his death in 1911, but Sherlock Holmes lives on in dozens of books and movies.

Exercise IV – Critical Reading Questions

1. Arthur Conan Doyle took an interest in Bell because of the doctor's
   A. abilities as a physician.
   B. powers of observation.
   C. interesting appearance.
   D. work as a detective.
   E. teaching methods.

2. Choose the lines from the passage that best support your answer to the previous question.
   A. "Bell's abilities made him a superior doctor. He became famous as a professor, teaching his methods to younger generations." (lines 19-20)
   B. "In 1888, he was called to investigate the Jack the Ripper murders in London." (lines 21-22)
   C. "Police efforts had not been sufficient enough to catch the murderer, who had already killed five people." (lines 22-23)
   D. "Arthur Conan Doyle was impressed by Bell's ability to notice details that anyone else would miss." (lines 26-27)
   E. "The Sherlock Holmes adventures were a source of pride for Dr. Bell." (line 39)

3. As it is used in line 14, the word *deduce* means
   A. think about.
   B. remove.
   C. argue about.
   D. discuss at length.
   E. figure out.

4. Dr. Bell inspired all of Sherlock Holmes's characteristics EXCEPT for his
   A. appearance.
   B. clothing.
   C. profession.
   D. intelligence.
   E. hobbies.

5. Choose the best title for this passage.
   A. The One and Only Sherlock Holmes
   B. Using the Powers of Observation to Solve Crime
   C. Doctor Joseph Bell: the Real Sherlock
   D. The Life of Arthur Conan Doyle
   E. The Difference Between Doctors and Detectives

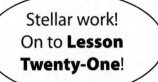

Stellar work!
On to **Lesson
Twenty-One**!

Lesson Twenty-One

bestow
BEH-**STOH**

v. to give as a reward or gift

When Princess Mia turned eighteen, the country *bestowed* on her the title of Queen of Genova.

syn: award

conserve
KUN-**SURV**

v. to use wisely and carefully

Turning the lights off when you leave the room will help to *conserve* energy.

syn: save　　　　　*ant: waste; misuse*

excess
EX-SES

adj. more than what is needed

Mom gives our *excess* chicken eggs to the family across the street.

syn: extra　　　　　*ant: lack*

hysterical
HIH-**STER**-IH-KULL

adj. uncontrollably emotional

The comedian's *hysterical* joke filled the whole room with laughter.

syn: hilarious　　　　*ant: calm; unmoved*

illusion
IH-**LOO**-ZHIN

n. something that is not real or what it appears to be

Mack the Magician is greatest at performing *illusions* that fool the audience.

syn: deception; trick

moderate
MAH-DUR-IT

adj. medium or average

A *moderate* amount of chocolate is fine, but eating too much can make you sick.

syn: modest; reasonable　　*ant: excessive*

restrain
RES-**TRAYN**

v. to keep under control

I pulled hard on Rex's leash to *restrain* him from chasing the squirrel.

syn: restrict　　　　*ant: release; allow*

savor
SAY-VUR

v. to take great pleasure in a taste, aroma, or experience

I ate the delicious burrito slowly so that I could *savor* the taste.

syn: enjoy   *ant: dislike*

vacant
VAY-KINT

adj. empty or unoccupied

Everyone was in town for the concert, so it was difficult to find a hotel with a *vacant* room left.

syn: empty   *ant: full*

wit
WIT

n. an ability to be intellectually clever or amusing

Doug knows how to use his *wit* to make people laugh.

syn: cleverness   *ant: dullness*

Exercise I – Words in Context

Using the list of vocabulary words, supply the correct word to complete each sentence.

1. While I am vacationing in Greece, my apartment in California will be _____.

2. Grandma Flo often _____ wisdom upon her many grandchildren.

3. Please grill my burger a[n] _____ amount—not so much that it is overcooked.

4. Molly donates money to groups that _____ areas for turtles to nest.

5. You need a strong _____ to succeed as a stand-up comedian.

6. The mirrors on the wall created the _____ that everyone looked larger than they really were.

7. Should we use the _____ material we didn't need for the dresses to make something else?

8. The most _____ part of the episode was when the monkey slipped on his own banana peel.

9. No one could _____ Ralph from running over to the ice cream truck.

10. Dad finds it difficult to _____ his lunch because he's usually in a big hurry to get back to work.

Exercise II – Finish the Sentence

First, choose the ending for each sentence that makes the best sense with the italicized vocabulary word used. Then, write your own ending for each sentence that shows you understand the meaning of the vocabulary word.

1. The football player said that he did only *moderate* exercise; I agree because…
    A. he spends hours lifting weights almost every day.
    B. he goes to the gym once a week and sometimes less.

2. We looked into our friend's living room, saw that it was *vacant*, and…
    A. decided to play a board game together.
    B. wondered where he had gone.

3. The speech wasn't that *hysterical* in my opinion, so I couldn't understand why…
    A. my sister could not stop laughing.
    B. Dad looked upset at everything he heard.

4. The man's eyes in that painting seemed to follow me around the room, but I knew it was an *illusion* because…
    A. paintings cannot really move.
    B. the artist had added moving robotic eyes.

5. The car was able to drive in *excess* of…
    A. 150 miles per hour.
    B. the damage to its bumper.

6. *Conserve* your strength if you expect…
    A. to win the pie-eating competition.
    B. to be hiking in the wilderness for a while.

7. Because Annie is full of *wit*, she…
    A. tends to act shy at parties.
    B. always makes her guests laugh.

8. It's difficult to *restrain* ourselves from talking when…
    A. we're in the library studying.
    B. we visit the natural history museum.

9. When she *bestowed* her father's name on me, my mom…

    A. had chosen it out of a book of baby names.

    B. showed how much her dad meant to her.

10. I sat in the restaurant for an hour and *savored*…

    A. the delicious steak dinner.

    B. my water as I waited for the check.

Exercise III – Crossword Puzzle

Use the clues and the words from this lesson to complete the crossword puzzle.

Across

3. Some people believe any dumb _____ they see on TV, like the one showing an alien ship hovering over a donut shop.

6. The horror movie frightened my little brother, and he became _____, thinking the monster was outside the house.

8. The hurricane covered three states, but we were lucky, and only a[n] _____ amount of rain landed on our city.

9. The drooling beagle _____ the smell of the steaks sizzling on the barbecue grill.

10. "_____ yourselves and don't push; there's enough birthday cake for everyone," said Mike.

Down

1. I saw my dad's joke book on his desk and looked at it, but I didn't get most of the _____; he thinks they are very funny, though.

2. The hikers were hungry, but they had to _____ the small amount of food they had left, or they would run out before they got home.

4. The _____ fuel leaked over the top of the storage tank.

5. President Harrison _____ medals for bravery on two sergeants and one major.

7. When we looked into the cage, we saw it was _____ and assumed that the lion had escaped.

Exercise IV – Improving Paragraphs

Carefully read the passage and then choose the best answer for each of the questions.
The questions will ask you to make changes to improve the writing of the passage.

1   [1] In the 1960s, Costa Rica had a major problem: Its tropical rain forests were disappearing. [2] Loggers and ranchers cut down trees as fast as they could, either to sell the wood or to create **vacant** areas for farming or raising cattle. [3] Since the 1960s, more than half of the jungle has disappeared. [4] The destruction of forests in Costa Rica was a serious issue. [5] People proposed many solutions, but few could balance making money and saving the environment. [6] That's why Costa Rica and other countries facing similar troubles created ecotourism programs. [7] Ecotourism is a form of **conservation** that helps the economy while protecting the land. **{1}**

2   In 1970, Costa Rica established the National Park Service and created the country's first protected parks. The parks were designed to protect the region's ecology. **{2}** The number of national parks has since been increased by Costa Rica. The number of management efforts has since been increased by Costa Rica. Twenty-one percent of Costa Rican territory is now protected. The parks successfully **restrained** deforestation and reduced jungle losses to **moderate** levels.

3   [1] Today, however, ecotourism is thriving.[2] **{3}** costa rica is a country in Central america, not far from tens of millions of vacationers. [3] It is one of few countries to border both the Atlantic and Pacific Oceans. [4] It is home to hundreds of thousands of breathtaking animal and plant species, as well as amazing beaches, rainforests, mountains, and volcanoes. [5] More than three out of four tourists travel to Costa Rica just to **savor** the gorgeous scenery and wildlife. [6] Visitors can live in small jungle resorts, hike jungle trails, and go snorkeling among the coral reefs. [7] They get to see rare animals and plants in their natural habitats instead of in zoos or greenhouses. [8] The money gives jobs to thousands, and it pays to continue protecting the nature of Costa Rica. [9] **{4}** For the first few years, the Costa Rican government was uncertain about ecotourism.

4   As good as it might sound, ecotourism is not perfect. With a million tourists visiting every year, environmentalists worry that there is an **excess** of traffic in some of the natural areas. Not all trails can handle thousands of hikers every year. The soil loosens and washes away in rainstorms. Some people litter and disturb wildlife habitats. Though the damage isn't as bad as destroying rainforests, ecotourism, too, must be kept under control in order to preserve Costa Rica's natural treasures. **{5}**

Exercise IV – Improving Paragraphs Questions

1. Choose the sentence from paragraph 1 that can be deleted because it repeats information.
  A. sentence 2
  B. sentence 4
  C. sentence 6
  D. sentence 7

2. The author would like to combine the underlined sentences. Choose the best way to combine the sentences.

  "The number of national parks has since been increased by Costa Rica. The number of management efforts has since been increased by Costa Rica."

  A. The number of national parks has since been increased by Costa Rica and the number of management efforts has since been increased by Costa Rica.
  B. Costa Rica has since increased the number of national parks and management efforts.
  C. The number of national parks has since been increased by Costa Rica and has also increase the number of management efforts.
  D. The number of national parks has increased, and management efforts have since increased by Costa Rica.

3. Choose the best revision of the underlined portion of the sentence.
  A. Costa Rica is a country in Central America
  B. costa Rica is a Country in central america
  C. Costa Rica is a country central america
  D. Costa rica is a country in central America

4. Sentence 9 is out of place in paragraph 3. Choose the point to which the writer should move the sentence.
  A. before sentence 7
  B. before sentence 5
  C. before sentence 4
  D. before sentence 1

5. The author would like to add the following sentence to the passage.

  "Tourists spend millions of dollars on resorts, food, guides, and transportation."

  Choose the best paragraph in which to place this sentence.
  A. paragraph 1
  B. paragraph 2
  C. paragraph 3
  D. paragraph 4

Review: Lessons 19-21

Exercise I – Related Words

Choose the word that best completes the sentence.

1. The _____ lived in an *abode* that looked like a castle from a fairy tale.
   A. wit
   B. diagram
   C. omnivore
   D. artifact
   E. monarch

2. When our friend moved away, Harry *grieved* quietly, but I was _____ for a week.
   A. vacant
   B. superior
   C. offensive
   D. hysterical
   E. vague

3. Two burgers would be _____ for lunch; any more would be an *excess* of food.
   A. sufficient
   B. spiritual
   C. moderate
   D. rural
   E. wholesome

4. The drama club _____ Diana from the musical because she had *acquired* a part-time job and missed too many rehearsals.
   A. reprimanded
   B. bestowed
   C. restrained
   D. expelled
   E. conserved

5. I am awful at hockey; even if you had only _____ skill in the sport, you'd still be *superior* to me.

    A. vague

    B. moderate

    C. vacant

    D. wholesome

    E. hysterical

6. Grandpa *bestowed* on me a[n] _____ that has been handed down through the family for generations.

    A. symptom

    B. monarch

    C. artifact

    D. excess

    E. illusion

7. "We must _____ the environment hippos need so that we don't *endanger* them further," said the zoologist.

    A. conserve

    B. savor

    C. grieve

    D. expel

    E. acquire

8. I had to _____ myself from yelling at Dylan for his *offensive* comments.

    A. merge

    B. expel

    C. endanger

    D. savor

    E. restrain

Exercise II – Synonyms and Antonyms

Match the word with its synonym.

1. _____ offensive

2. _____ grieve

3. _____ merge

4. _____ rural

5. _____ superior

6. _____ restrain

7. _____ wholesome

A. rustic

B. restrict

C. mourn

D. extraordinary

E. respectable

F. combine

G. horrible

Match the word with its antonym.

8. _____ vague

9. _____ sufficient

10. _____ reprimand

11. _____ moderate

12. _____ hysterical

13. _____ endanger

14. _____ conserve

H. calm

I. definite

J. protect

K. lacking

L. waste

M. excessive

N. praise